# Contents

# 01

# Street works and road works

## Contents



## Supporting information

### G: Checklists and forms



### GT 700 Toolbox talks

F
01

## Overview

**The New Roads and Street Works Act (NRSWA) provides a legislative framework for street works (including by public utility companies). In recent years the Health and Safety Executive (HSE) has expressed concern at the number of workers and members of the public killed or seriously injured through accidents related to road works.**

## 1.1 Introduction

Road works will almost always bring the workers carrying out construction work into close proximity with vehicles (both construction plant and passing traffic). The safety of the workers and vehicle drivers/operators will depend upon the works being properly planned, carried out by trained and qualified workers and the behaviour of the passing traffic.

> **The Highways Term Maintenance Association (HTMA) has stated that 'it is not only oncoming vehicles that pose a threat to road workers but the behaviour of drivers in passing vehicles is a growing concern. Road workers have experienced the throwing of missiles (often food and bottles), verbal abuse as well as personal injury caused by road users' vehicles'.**

Britain's roads are extremely busy. In terms of overall road safety, current national figures show a decline in road accident casualties over the past 40 years. However, injuries to the 40,000 workers on Britain's roads have risen.

In today's traffic conditions, the live carriageway of any highway is a very dangerous place to work.

Drivers ignoring temporary speed limits is commonplace, leaving road workers even more vulnerable, with very little to protect them from approaching vehicles.

In an attempt to improve the situation, the Highways Agency (HA) introduced a road worker action plan, with the theme of zero harm. The HA's aim is to reduce the risks to the health and safety of road workers by working in partnership with service providers and others to improve training and performance, and by changing the way that operations are carried out on the road network. Some examples are shown below.

- Removing road workers from the live carriageway whenever possible.
- Reducing the exposure to risk whenever anyone is working on the road network.
- Highlighting the importance of road workers and their safety to road users to influence driver behaviour.
- Improving communication methods on road worker safety issues throughout Government and supply chain forums to give a consistent approach to improved performance.
- Continually reviewing working practices to reduce the risk to road workers, including the introduction of local targets, investigating layout changes and trialling new technologies.
- Reducing speed and improving compliance through road works, including the use of average speed detection.

For its part, the Highways Term Maintenance Association (HTMA), through its members and safety working group, has actively supported the HA in delivering the aims of the road worker action plan.

> **A study by Oxford University ranked working on the highway as the sixteenth most hazardous occupation in the United Kingdom.**

## 1.2 Important points

- All work must be carried out in accordance with the *Safety at street works and road works – A Code of Practice* (rewritten in 2013 and in force from October 2014).
- Site-specific risk assessments must be carried out.
- Works include any placement, connection or maintenance of temporary or permanent services, pipes, cables, sewers or drains that are laid or located within the carriageway or footway. This also includes forming new or temporary entrances and roads where they join an existing highway or footpath.
- Road users, whether in a vehicle or on foot, approaching the works on the road or footway, from any direction, must be able to understand exactly what is happening and what is expected of them.

- ☑ The Code of Practice (CoP), often referred to as the *Red book*, that supports the legislation must be complied with. The CoP is for works on all highways and roads, except motorways and dual carriageways with a speed limit of 50 mph or more. The CoP specifies minimum safety requirements for:
  - signage, lighting and guarding
  - methods of traffic control
  - controlling the speed of passing traffic
  - works near to tramways and railways, equipment and vehicles.
- ☑ Operatives who carry out work on the highway must be competent to do so, particularly anyone involved in laying out the site, positioning signage or lighting, implementing traffic control measures and undertaking similar jobs.

## 1.3 Legislative requirements

There are three pieces of legislation that all have an impact upon the way that road works are carried out. The main relevant requirements are outlined below.

www. **Copies of all legislation can be found online.**

### 1.3.1 New Roads and Street Works Act

- ☑ Applies to works carried out in a street by an undertaker exercising a statutory right to inspect, place and maintain pipes, cables, sewers or drains, which are laid in the carriageway or footway. The term undertaker also covers holders of street works licences.
- ☑ Provides a legislative framework for street works by undertakers (including public utilities).
- ☑ Created a number of criminal offences that are triable in Magistrates' Courts (Sheriffs' Courts in Scotland). Amongst the 20 possible offences are:
  - failing to carry out works safely (such as signing, lighting and guarding)
  - not having supervisors and operatives, or either, with the relevant prescribed qualifications
  - failing to complete the contracted works within a reasonable timescale.

When a Local Authority acts as an agent to an undertaker or contractor to carry out work for an undertaker, the execution of the works is governed by the Act.

*Workers levelling ground for new road*

The efficient co-ordination of street works is one of the most important aspects of street works legislation, benefiting street authorities, undertakers and road users alike. The main objectives of the New Roads and Street Works Act (NRSWA) are shown below.

- ☑ Ensure safety.
- ☑ Minimise inconvenience to people using a street, including a specific reference to people with a disability.
- ☑ Protect the structure of the street and the apparatus in it.

The Act comprises of the following parts.

- ☑ Part 1. New Roads in England and Wales.
- ☑ Part 2. New Roads in Scotland.
- ☑ Part 3. Street Works in England and Wales.
- ☑ Part 4. Road Works in Scotland.
- ☑ Part 5. General.
- ☑ Associated schedules.

### 1.3.2 Highways Act

- ☑ Was introduced to tackle congestion and disruption on the road network.
- ☑ Places a duty on local traffic authorities to ensure the expeditious movement of traffic on their road network and those networks of surrounding authorities.
- ☑ Gives authorities additional tools to better manage parking policies, moving traffic enforcement and the co-ordination of street works.
- ☑ Empowers the Highway Authorities to impose conditions on those working on the highway. It makes provision for licences for skips and scaffolds and places responsibility for safety with the Highway Authority. Contractors must obtain permission before working on the highway.
- ☑ Applies to all work on the highway. The Highway Authority (or Roads Authority in Scotland) must be consulted and grant permission for works to be carried out. This applies to any works for road construction or maintenance purposes.

### 1.3.3 Traffic Management Act

- ☑ Places a duty on street authorities (such as County Councils), to secure more efficient use of their networks, to avoid or reduce traffic congestion and disruption and to regulate the use of the network.
- ☑ Requires a contractor who will be working on the road to provide notice in advance of all works that directly or indirectly affect the highway network, effectively booking the road space. Minimum notice periods for different categories of work are contained within the NRSWA.
- ☑ Empowers Local Authorities to introduce a permitting scheme, which is designed to control the carrying out of specified works, in specified streets, in a specified area. In doing this it replaces the notice system under the NRSWA, whereby utility companies informed Highway Authorities of their intentions to carry out works in their areas.

### 1.3.4 Non-statutory guidance on safety at street works

Published by the Department for Transport, the *Traffic signs manual* contents are instructional for roads, parking, road management and traffic signs.

It gives guidance on the use of traffic signs and road markings prescribed by the Traffic Signs Regulations and covers England, Wales, Scotland and Northern Ireland. Revised editions of the manual will be published here as they are released.

www.

**The chapters may be purchased in hard copy from TSO or freely downloaded from the DTi website.**

**Chapter 1. Introduction.** Introduction and an outline of the historical, functional and design aspects of signs. The chapter includes sections dealing with the positioning and mounting of signs.

**Chapter 2. Informatory signs.** Chapter 2 is currently draft and a work in progress. It will contain advice on the design and use of directional signs, and also other informatory signs (such as 'Home zone' signs). Due to the amount of work required to complete Chapter 2, it is intended that interim advice on individual topics will be made available as and when completed.

The current advice on the design and use of directional informatory signs is published in Local Transport Note (LTN) 1/94. Also available is the latest list of primary destinations in England, which supersedes the information in LTN 1/94, and guidance on the calculation of x-heights, which is site-specific and more accurate than the table in LTN 1/94.

**Chapter 3. Regulatory signs.** Gives guidelines on the correct use of regulatory signs prescribed by the Traffic Signs Regulations. These include prohibited turns, waiting and loading restrictions, bus and cycle lanes, and so on. There is also a comprehensive section dealing with the signing of speed limits.

**Chapter 4. Warning signs.** Warning signs are used to alert drivers to potential danger ahead. They indicate a need for special caution by road users and may require a reduction in speed or some other manoeuvre. This reprinted edition includes four minor amendments and addition of Appendix A, Note 7.

**Chapter 5. Road markings.** Road markings serve a very important function in conveying to road users information and requirements that might not be possible using upright signs. They have the advantage that they can often be seen when a verge-mounted sign is obscured, and, unlike such signs, they can provide a continuing message.

**Chapter 7. The design of traffic signs.** How sign faces are designed. This chapter does not include the various methods by which signs are constructed and mounted. It supersedes Local Transport Note *'2/94 Directional informatory signs interim design notes'*, which was **withdrawn in 1997**.

**Chapter 8 (Part 1). Road works and temporary situations – Design.** Guidance for the design of temporary traffic management arrangements, which should be implemented to facilitate maintenance work, or in response to temporary situations.

**Chapter 8 (Part 2). Road works and temporary situations – Operations.** Guidance for planning, managing, and participating in operations to implement, maintain and remove temporary traffic management arrangements.

## 1.4 Safety at street works and road works – A Code of Practice

This updated CoP came into force on 1 October 2014. The first print run contained a list of amendments for users to update manually. Therefore, readers are strongly advised to ensure they use the second print, which incorporates all of the additional amendments; the version annotated '2nd impression (with amendments), June 2014'.

This CoP is a pocket-size reference book, intended to be used at the place of work. Its content is aimed at all workers on site but it does not attempt to cover every situation.

The authorities with responsibility for road maintenance in England, Wales and Northern Ireland **must** comply with the CoP for their own works. In Scotland, the roads authority **should** comply with the CoP for their works, as recommended by Scottish ministers.

Within the code, wherever the term *highways authorities* appears, it should be taken to refer to the roads authorities in Scotland and Northern Ireland. Failure to comply with the CoP is a criminal offence, potentially leading to prosecution and civil proceedings (except in Scotland).

The CoP is applicable to all highways and roads, except motorways and dual carriageways with a speed limit of 50 mph or more. It does not apply to skips or scaffolding located in the highway.

Anyone contemplating work on the highway, particularly anyone new to this type of work, must obtain and refer to it as necessary. It is very easy to use, and it would be difficult to argue that anyone who is managing a project that involves work in the highway should not have a copy. It would normally form part of the safety management system for whoever is doing the traffic management, and checking the site set-up against the layout drawing is a quick and simple way to audit site procedures.

Whilst a supervisor qualified under the New Roads and Street Works Act will know what to do in most situations, it is the employer's responsibility to ensure that safe procedures are in place and followed and proper arrangements for supervision are in place.

**Road users, including pedestrians, cyclists and horse riders, should not be put at risk and should be able to see the extent and nature of any risk before they reach it.**

**The Code of Practice can be freely downloaded from the Department for Transport's website, or it can be purchased from TSO.**

**For more detailed advice on subjects not covered in the Code of Practice refer to Chapter 8 of the *Traffic signs manual*, which can also be freely downloaded.**

## 1.5 Carrying out road works

### 1.5.1 Before starting work

As for other construction projects, all road works will fall within the requirements of the Construction (Design and Management) Regulations to a greater or lesser degree. A construction phase plan will be required for all construction projects. If required, a principal designer and principal contractor must also be appointed and the principal contractor or contractor must actively manage health and safety on site.

Before starting any work on the carriageway or footway, there are specific notice periods for informing the Highway/Streets Authority (or, in Scotland, the Roads Authority) that you intend to start work.

Depending upon where the work is being carried out, the Streets Authority may well be the Local Authority, the County Council, the Department for Transport, or even the County Council on behalf of the Department for Transport, local Government and regions. The principal or main contractor must check to establish to whom they are responsible, and to whom they should give notice.

### 1.5.2 Co-ordination of road works

When notice is given to the HA that the work is planned, they will inform the other utility undertakers in an attempt to co-ordinate works during a single excavation in order to avoid the same piece of roadway being continually excavated.

### 1.5.3 Major works

The term **major works** covers works carried out by the Highway Authority, which could include the following.

- ☑ The reconstruction or widening of the highway.
- ☑ Works on dual carriageways and at roundabouts.
- ☑ Other similar major works.
- ☑ The construction of vehicle crossings over footways and verges.

### 1.5.4 Diversionary works

The term **diversionary works** covers works to:

- ☑ protect apparatus on site
- ☑ relocate apparatus elsewhere.

The CoP contains comprehensive information on the responsibilities of the various utility undertakers and highway authorities relating to major road works that may affect the safety of apparatus and the need to divert apparatus.

The information includes guiding principles and outlines considerations that should be taken into account and the procedures to be followed.

**Apparatus**

Any pipe or ducting buried within the highway or pavement that is owned by one of the utilities. (Examples of apparatus are gas pipes, water mains, sewers, electricity cables, telephone cables and fibre optic communications cables.)

F
01

**Unexpected damage to, or disconnection of, any apparatus could have serious implications for many people who are totally unconnected with the work.**

Construction work, which may put apparatus at risk, includes the following.

- The removal of the footway or carriageway construction.
- Construction plant crossing or working in the vicinity of apparatus.
- The undermining or removal of side support to apparatus.
- Any deep excavation adjacent to apparatus.
- Piling or ground consolidation operations.

These risks can be minimised by:

- providing suitable and safe vehicle crossing and access points (see below)
- temporarily moving apparatus to a safe location during the construction work
- protecting or temporarily supporting apparatus in situ.

**Methods of supporting apparatus during excavation form part of the assessment process incorporated within the relevant operative and supervisor qualifications.**

The correct construction of vehicle crossings is important as otherwise the works could put apparatus at risk in a number of ways, as a result of the following.

- The majority of service apparatus is located in footways.
- Footway construction layers must normally be excavated to accommodate thicker construction layers.
- The new construction may no longer provide adequate cover to apparatus.
- The vehicular loading may be greater than the apparatus can withstand.
- Vibrations from vehicles may weaken joints over a period of time.

## 1.5.5 Excavations

In many cases digging trenches will form a part of road works. It is therefore essential that such excavations meet the following requirements.

- Only commenced when it has been established that it is safe to do so.
- Adequately guarded where necessary to prevent the public or construction workers being put at risk of falls.
- Supported where the risk assessment shows that it would be unsafe not to do so.
- Fitted with lights at night where otherwise construction workers or the public would be put at risk of falling.
- Equipped with dewatering equipment where necessary.
- Equipped with forced ventilation where otherwise a build-up of hazardous vapour would occur.

There may be occasions where trenchless technology (such as pipe-jacking or thrust-boring) lends itself to the job in hand, although the use of such methods must first be cleared with the client and designers of the scheme.

**For further details on safe working in or near to excavations refer to Chapter D07 Excavations.**

## 1.6 Safety of gas apparatus

### 1.6.1 Depth of cover

The normal minimum depth of cover for gas mains operating in the low and medium pressure ranges is:

- ☑ 600 mm in footways or verges
- ☑ 750 mm in carriageways.

However, in practice these depths may vary, as each area gas board can have its own standards.

In certain circumstances, depending upon the mains material, operating pressure and depth of cover, it may be acceptable for the mains to remain in situ when only subjected to light traffic (for example, a vehicle layby or crossing). It is not generally permissible to allow cast iron mains previously in the footway or verge to be subjected to vehicular traffic.

### 1.6.2 Risks during construction

Liaison with the gas undertaker during the planning stage is essential because existing mains, specifically older materials (such as cast iron), cannot be raised, lowered or moved laterally even for a few millimetres without risk. Gas apparatus must not be undermined and certain apparatus is particularly vulnerable to deep excavations adjacent to the apparatus.

Any proposals to dig deep trenches may mean that gas apparatus will have to be diverted.

## 1.7 Safety of water apparatus

Decisions on the protection or diversion of water mains are likely to be influenced by considerations of access to mains for repair purposes.

### 1.7.1 Depth of cover

The minimum depth of cover for the three types of water mains (trunk mains, distributor mains and service pipes) will vary according to its type.

Further information can be found in the CoP, and by consulting with the water company in whose area you are working.

### 1.7.2 Risks during construction

Construction plant and lorries travelling over water apparatus with temporarily reduced cover can be an unacceptable risk. Therefore, diversions may be necessary unless protective measures are practicable.

Factors influencing the decision to divert water pipes must include the following.

- ☑ The maintenance of the continuity of supply and the water quality.
- ☑ Material types and condition.
- ☑ The inability to raise, lower or slew pipes.
- ☑ The possible loss of ground support to pipes with the consequential risk of damage.

## 1.8 Safety of telecommunications apparatus

The need for the rigorous exclusion of moisture from telecommunication cables and joints places constraints on the extent to which older cables can be moved during works.

For maintenance purposes there is the added need for vehicles to have access and be located at or near jointing chambers.

### 1.8.1 Preferred depth of cover

Varying depths of cover may be found with this type of equipment, depending on the types and design of the cables. As a rough guide, television and telecom cabling can be found at depths varying from 250 mm in the verge or footway up to 900 mm in the carriageway.

### 1.8.2 Risks during construction

According to circumstances, the apparatus may be left in situ if ducts are adequately protected from construction plant and vehicles by the use of metal plates or tracks.

In some cases, it may be possible to accommodate small, temporary or permanent alterations in the line of a duct track by bodily slewing, raising or lowering a nest of ducts with the cables in situ.

### 1.8.3 Overhead telecommunication lines

Poles must be positioned to:

- ☑ minimise the risk of damage to cables by vehicles
- ☑ give the minimum inconvenience to pedestrians
- ☑ avoid obstructing access to premises.

Road alterations may necessitate the replacement of poles if the clearance under the cables becomes inadequate.

Minimum heights above ground for overhead telecommunication lines are typically:

- ☑ 5.5 m at any point over a street
- ☑ 6.1 m on bus routes
- ☑ 6.5 m on designated roads.

## 1.9 Safety of electrical apparatus

The following factors should be considered when protecting cables in situ or diverting apparatus.

### 1.9.1 Underground cables

- ☑ The need to protect and support potentially hazardous equipment from mechanical impact, damage, strain and vibration during and after road works.
- ☑ A requirement to maintain the security of supply if alternative circuits are not available.
- ☑ The operating voltage of the apparatus.

The depth at which electricity cables or ducts are usually laid in the ground is decided by the need to avoid undue interference or damage.

Dependent on the type of cable and the power that it may be carrying, the depth of cover may vary from 450 mm up to 900 mm. It is common to find electrical cables much shallower than these depths, particularly over bridges or culverts, and extreme caution must be exercised.

In all cases, where the depth of cover is likely to increase or decrease, the apparatus owner must be consulted.

### 1.9.2 Overhead lines

- ☑ The supports and stays of overhead lines may have to be relocated.
- ☑ Ground clearance may be affected.
- ☑ Earth wires from supports may have to be re-sited.
- ☑ Underground pilot wires may be associated with the route of overhead lines.

The minimum height of overhead lines above ground varies according to the voltage of the cable and as directed by the service supplier. They can be as low as 5.2 m for lines carrying 33 kV, or up to 6.7 m for lines carrying 132 kV.

**Further information can be obtained from Chapter D08 Underground and overhead services, and in HSE Guidance Note GS6.**

### 1.9.3 Risks during construction

- ☑ Additional protection or temporary diversion may be necessary to prevent damage to any apparatus during the construction stage.
- ☑ The hazards of accidental electrical contact by persons on site must be fully assessed.
- ☑ Damage to underground cables can, in certain circumstances, cause widespread loss of electrical supplies for a long period.

## 1.10 Site layout definitions

**Works area** is the excavation, chamber, opening, reinstatement, and so on.

**Working space** is the space around the works area used to store tools, excavated material, equipment and plant.

It is also the space needed to move around the site without encroaching into live traffic or other hazards. Sufficient working space must be provided to ensure that the movement and operation of the plant (for example, swinging of jibs and excavator arms) is clear of passing traffic and is not encroaching into the safety zone.

**Safety zone** is the zone provided to protect site personnel from the traffic. No-one must enter the safety zone in the normal course of work. It is only necessary to enter the zone to maintain cones and other road signs. Materials and equipment must not be placed in the zone.

The safety zone comprises of the following.

- **Lead-in taper of cones (T).** The length will vary with the speed limit and the width of the works.
- **Longways clearance (L).** This is the distance between the lead-in taper of cones (T) and the working space. It will vary with the speed limit.
- **Sideways clearance (S).** This is the width between the working space and moving traffic. It will vary with the speed limit.

**For a chart showing the longways and sideways clearance dimensions required for works on roads with various speed limits refer to Appendix F.**

If an advisory speed limit is in operation this chart must be used to determine minimum longways and sideways clearances. Wherever traffic speeds are to be reduced, the method must be agreed in advance with the highway authority. For safety reasons, it may be necessary to advise emergency services of the location and duration of the works.

Working spaces and safety zones must be provided when personnel are present. If pedestrians are diverted into the carriageway, a safety zone must be provided between the outer pedestrian barrier and the traffic.

**For further information refer to Appendix C and also page 34 of the CoP.**

Where the highway width is so restricted as to prohibit the provision of the appropriate sideways clearance and diversion of traffic would be impractical, traffic speeds must be reduced to less than 10 mph and a mandatory speed limit imposed. There must also be an agreed safe method of working imposed on the site.

This method of working, which must be decided in advance of the work, should preclude working in the safety zone wherever possible. It is also advisable that it should be recorded in writing.

## 1.11 Signage and other site equipment

Traffic signs and other apparatus for the control of traffic must comply with the **Traffic Signs Regulations and General Directions**. (These were under consultation until June 2014, with a view to a revised version coming into force in 2015.) Compliance is achieved by the use of equipment conforming to the relevant British Standards. Equipment must also meet any requirements set out in the code as to size or performance.

All street works, irrespective of site and whether taking place at ground level or overhead, require adequate warning and information to be given to pedestrians and drivers.

The sequence for setting out signs is shown in the images below.

### e.g. Setting out signs

**For a selection of signs and equipment refer to Appendix A.**

F
01

### 1.11.1 Crossing high-speed roads on foot

The HSE was so concerned about this aspect of temporary traffic management works that it published specific guidance on it, which applies to motorways and dual carriageways with a speed limit of 50 mph and above.

**For further information refer to the HSE publication *Crossing high-speed roads on foot during temporary traffic management works* (CIS53).**

The guidance puts the initial onus on the designers of road works to ensure that the risk arising from the installation, alteration and removal of temporary traffic management aspects of their designs are assessed and, where reasonably practicable, eliminated or reduced. Any remaining significant risks should be highlighted and subsequently controlled by the careful planning and management of the works.

Systems of work should not rely on workers crossing the carriageway unless there are:

- ☑ adequate sight lines
- ☑ traffic flows in which there are suitable gaps
- ☑ no more than four continuous lanes to cross (including slip roads)
- ☑ a central reservation that provides a safe place to work.

Traffic management workers require standards of physical fitness, eyesight and hearing. Their health should be assessed before they are assigned to traffic management work. Health assessment should ensure that workers:

- ☑ have full use of neck, trunk and legs
- ☑ have at least 6/12 distance vision when wearing glasses or contact lenses
- ☑ have good hearing
- ☑ are suitable for this work if they suffer from specific conditions (such as vertigo, balance disorders, gastrointestinal conditions and sleep disorders)
- ☑ are not taking inappropriate medication, illegal drugs or excessive amounts of alcohol.

### 1.11.2 Advance signs

A 'Road works ahead' sign must be placed in a conspicuous position well before the works.

Its size and minimum distance from the start of the lead-in taper is governed by road type and traffic speed.

**For further information refer to page 21 of the CoP.**

A 'Road narrows ahead' sign, indicating which side of the carriageway is obstructed, should be placed between the 'Road works ahead' sign and commencement of the taper of cones.

### 1.11.3 Cones and lights

Traffic cones are placed to guide the traffic past the works.

The length of coned area and size of cones is governed by the speed limit and the type of road.

**For further information refer to Appendix A.**

Road warning lights are added at night, in poor daytime visibility and in bad weather. They must not be positioned higher than 1.2 m above the road surface.

**For further information refer to the CoP.**

Road warning lights are used as shown in the table below.

| Warning lights | Lights can be used | | Lights must be used | | |
|---|---|---|---|---|---|
| **Speed limit** | 20 mph | 30 mph | 40 mph | 50 mph | 60 mph |
| **Maximum height** | 1.5 m | 1.5 m | 1.5 m | 1.2 m | 1.2 m |
| **Flashing option permitted (on street lit roads only)?** | Yes | Yes | Yes | No | No |

### 1.11.4 Keep left and keep right signs

Place 'Keep left' or 'Keep right' signs as appropriate at the beginning and end of the lead-in taper of cones.

### 1.11.5 Traffic barrier or lane closed sign

A traffic barrier is positioned within the coned-off area facing oncoming traffic to indicate the width of works site.

If a conspicuous vehicle is present, a barrier may not be necessary. *(For further information refer to 1.12.6 Works on footways.)*

### 1.11.6 Pedestrian barriers

All sides of an excavation where a pedestrian may gain access must be fenced off.

### 1.11.7 Information board

An information board **must** be displayed at all sites, except mobile sites, short duration works and minor works that do not involve excavation. On sites where it is not a mandatory requirement, it is still desirable that a board is displayed.

As a minimum, the following information must be provided on the board.

- ☑ The name of the organisation undertaking the works.
- ☑ A telephone number for emergencies.
- ☑ The name of the principal contractor.

Wherever practical, the board should also contain other useful information, such as a description of the work that is being carried out, how long the work will take and a message apologising for any delay or inconvenience.

### 1.11.8 End sign

Road works that are 50 m or more in length (excluding the length of the tapers) must have a 'Road works ahead' sign and an 'End' plate, beyond the end of the works, to indicate the end of the work and any associated restrictions. Where there are a series of two or more sites close together, the 'End' sign should only be placed after the last site. (Remember to cater to traffic travelling in both directions.)

There is no need for an 'End' sign at the following locations.

- ☑ Where works are less than 50 m in length, unless there are two or more such sites close together.
- ☑ At road works on minor roads, with a speed limit of 30 mph or less, that do not carry a heavy volume of traffic or many large vehicles.

Where the permanent speed limit changes within the section of a road covered by the temporary speed restriction, any signs indicating the permanent speed limit must be obscured. Signs indicating the permanent speed limit must be positioned, on both sides of the carriageway, at the end of the temporary speed restriction, to indicate the speed limit from that point on.

**For further information refer to the CoP.**

### 1.11.9 Sign lighting and reflectorisation

Signs and any plates used with them must be directly lit when all of the following conditions apply.

- ☑ There is a permanent speed limit of 50 mph or above.
- ☑ There is general street lighting.
- ☑ The street lighting is on.
- ☑ The sign is within 50 m of a street light.

All signs, including cones and red and white barrier planks, must be reflectorised to BS 873-6:1983 Class 1 or Class 2. The only exception is the information board and pedestrian signs.

**For further information refer to the CoP.**

### 1.11.10 Security and stability of signs

Only use signs that are approved and in accordance with the relevant British Standard, and ensure that they are placed correctly.

Properly secure all signs and guarding equipment, so that they cannot be blown over by the wind or dislodged by passing traffic. Use sacks containing sand or other fine granular materials. Do not use kerbstones or similar weights for this purpose, as they could be dangerous if hit by moving traffic.

Make sure that the signs are correctly positioned and of adequate size to give early warning of the hazard, in accordance with the table in the CoP.

Check the signs regularly for both position and cleanliness as they may have been moved, damaged or become dirty.

### 1.11.11 Visibility of signs

All signs must be reflectorised and adequately lit after dark in accordance with the CoP. Signs must be placed so as to give the required forward visibility to approaching vehicles.

**For sizing and siting distances of signage and cones refer to Appendix F.**

### 1.11.12 Two-way roads

On a two-way road, the signs should be set out for traffic in both directions.

### 1.11.13 Surplus signs

Any signs or guarding equipment no longer required and left in position, either during or on completion of the work, will be illegal. Remove them immediately.

## 1.12 Traffic control

Select the method of traffic control from the table within the CoP. The CoP gives precise details of these methods.

**You will also need to refer to the table in the inside back cover of the CoP (also included at Appendix F).**

**For examples of diagrams on how to manage traffic control refer to Appendix B.**

### 1.12.1 Road widths

For two-way traffic, minimum road widths are shown below.

- ☑ 6.75 m on bus and HGV routes.
- ☑ 5.5 m on other roads for cars and light vehicles.

Any width less than 5.5 m is too narrow for two-way traffic and so the width must be reduced to a maximum of 3.7 m and a traffic control system introduced.

For shuttle working, minimum road widths are shown below.

- ☑ **Buses and HGV routes:**
  - 3.25 metres desirable minimum width
  - 3 metres absolute minimum width.
- ☑ **Cars and light vehicles:**
  - 2.75 metres desirable minimum width
  - 2.5 metres absolute minimum width.

### 1.12.2 Traffic control by give and take system

Only use the give and take system when **all** the following apply.

- ☑ The length of the works from the start of the lead-in taper to the end of the exit taper is 50 m or less.
- ☑ Two-way traffic is less than 20 vehicles counted over three minutes (400 vehicles per hour).
- ☑ Fewer than 20 heavy goods vehicles pass the site per hour.
- ☑ The speed limit is 30 mph or under.
- ☑ Drivers approaching from either direction can see 50 m beyond the end of the works.

Parking near the works, especially in front and opposite, is controlled or prohibited, unless visibility or lane width is unaffected.

## 1.12.3 Traffic control by priority signs

Only use priority signs when **all** of the following apply.

- ☑ Two-way traffic is less than 42 vehicles, counted over three minutes (850 vehicles per hour).
- ☑ Length of works, including tapers, is no more than 80 m.
- ☑ Drivers approaching from either direction can see through the length of works from a specified distance 'D' before the works to a similar distance 'D' beyond the works. Distances vary according to speed restrictions, as follows:
  - 60 m on 30 mph roads
  - 70 m on 40 mph roads
  - 80 m on 50 mph roads
  - 100 m on 60 mph roads.

## 1.12.4 Traffic control by stop/go boards

This system may be used following consideration of the relation of two-way traffic flow to the length of the site. Details of limitations for using stop/go boards can be found in the CoP.

Where the shuttle lane with this type of system is more than 20 m, or it continues round a bend, stop/go boards will be needed at both ends of that lane.

## 1.12.5 Traffic control by portable traffic signals

Portable traffic signals may be used when the following requirements are met.

*Traffic control in operation on a private road*

- ☑ The speed limit is a maximum of 60 mph.
- ☑ The length of the site is 300 m or less.
- ☑ The site does not straddle a railway level crossing.
- ☑ The signals are of a type approved for use on the highway.
- ☑ Traffic control is at least 50 m away from a level crossing equipped with twin red light signals.
- ☑ The signals are vehicle actuated (unless otherwise instructed by the Highway Authority).
- ☑ The Highway Authority has been informed and, if to be used at a road junction, authorisation has been obtained.
- ☑ Stop/go boards are available in case the portable traffic signals cease to function correctly.

## 1.12.6 Works on footways

An alternative safe route for pedestrians must meet the following requirements.

*Footpath diversion showing the safe pedestrian route*

- ☑ Be provided if a footway or part of a footway is closed, before it is closed.
- ☑ Never be less than one metre wide and ideally be 1.5 m or more in width.
- ☑ Be equipped with kerb ramps or a raised footway, as may be necessary, to take account of the needs of children, the elderly, people with disabilities, particularly visual impairment, or those with prams or wheelchairs.
- ☑ Be a non-slip surface and free of trip hazards (laps on boarding may trip the elderly or infirm).
- ☑ Provide access to adjacent premises and public areas.

**For further information refer to Appendix C, and the CoP.**

## 1.12.7 Barriers

Pedestrian barriers should be used to mark out temporary footways, with a rigid barrier to protect pedestrians from traffic, excavation, plant or materials. Handrails should be between one metre and 1.2 m above ground level, with tapping rails 150 mm deep, set with the lower edge up to 200 mm above ground level.

Road warning lights should be placed at the ends of the barriers at night. Barriers may comprise separate portable post and plank systems, gate frames linked together, or semi-permanent constructions built to enclose the site.

There are several different requirements for the barrier planks associated with post and plank systems. The following explains the requirements and how they may be met using barrier planks, which are red and white and manufactured in fully retro-reflective materials.

**Retro-reflective means that at night the material reflects light back to the light source.**

Barrier planks are required to carry out three functions, shown in the table below.

| | | |
|---|---|---|
| 1. | As a **traffic barrier** | When a traffic lane is closed for works to take place, the regulations require this to be done with a retro-reflective red and white barrier plank placed across the lane. This is illustrated above *(in the traffic control photo)* as a traffic barrier ('Lane closed' sign) |
| 2. | As a **pedestrian barrier** | Pedestrians must be separated from the works by barriers, which are conspicuous and mounted as part of a portable fencing system. Pedestrian barrier planks may be of several different contrasting colours; yellow, white or orange colours are best detected by partially-sighted people, but red and white is one of the acceptable combinations |
| 3. | As a **tapping rail** for blind and partially-sighted people | Tapping rails are placed as the bottom rail in a pedestrian fencing system. A red and white barrier plank may be used |

***Note:*** *from 1 April 2015 in Scotland, there is an additional requirement that where a site is unattended for a period of 24 hours or more (including weekends), individual barriers or groups of barriers must be capable of withstanding winds of Class B (17.6 m/s) blowing from any direction.*

All barriers facing vehicular traffic should be of the fully retro-reflective red and white form. Red and white barrier planks do not have to be used for pedestrian barriers or tapping rails but, if they are, they must be retro-reflective. Other planks used for these purposes do not need to be retro-reflective.

There are other points to note about the use of barrier planks in portable fencing systems.

- ☑ The traffic barrier ('Lane closed' sign) is not needed if the works are protected by a conspicuous vehicle.
- ☑ Pedestrian barrier systems must be rigid enough to guard pedestrians from traffic, excavations, plant or materials. They must be placed with sufficient clearance to prevent pedestrians falling into the excavation and, when placed to create a temporary footway in the carriageway parallel to the traffic stream, must be protected by a row of traffic cones between the barrier and the traffic stream. Consult your supervisor if the excavation is deep, or positioned close to pedestrians, as stronger barriers may be needed and/or other safety measures may be required (such as covering or temporarily refilling the excavation).
- ☑ Where a work site may be approached by pedestrians crossing the road from the opposite side, you should place barriers, including tapping rails, all around the excavation, even when pedestrians are not diverted into the carriageway.
- ☑ Where long excavations are sited in situations where pedestrians are not expected to cross from the opposite side, barriers on the traffic stream side of the works area do not need the tapping rail. In these circumstances, on an unrestricted road, the barrier on the traffic stream side can be replaced with an additional row of cones. These cones should be linked with a suitably supported traffic tape to attract attention to the boundary of the safety zone.

Use pedestrian barriers to mark out any temporary footway. You must always use a rigid barrier to protect pedestrians from traffic, excavations, plant or materials. Place road warning lights at the ends of the barriers at night so that they may be clearly seen by pedestrians.

**For further information refer to the CoP.**

## 1.13 Personal protective equipment

### 1.13.1 High-visibility clothing

Given the nature of road works and the proximity of moving traffic, the importance of workers being clearly seen by colleagues and the travelling public cannot be overstated. Whether working on site or just visiting, everyone must wear a high-visibility jacket or waistcoat at all times, manufactured to BS EN 471.

*Workers wearing PPE to Class 3 standard*

High-visibility clothing must conform to the relevant, current British or European standards and be worn as listed below.

- ☑ When operating outside of the working space (such as when setting out, maintaining or removing signing, lighting, guarding and temporary traffic control).
- ☑ Where necessary, within the working space, as directed by the employer.
- ☑ Correctly fastened.
- ☑ In a clean and usable condition.

#### 1.13.1.1 England and Northern Ireland

A risk assessment must determine the standard of high-visibility clothing required. In most cases, for work outside the working area, the likely minimum requirement is for a jacket with the maximum area of visible material, as specified in current British and European standards.

### 1.13.1.2 Scotland and Wales

In Scotland and Wales the general requirement is for a jacket to have full length sleeves and comply with current British and European standards. However, where a risk assessment indicates that full length sleeves would increase the risk of harm, due to the activity being carried out, three-quarter length sleeves may be worn.

The table below gives an indication of the requirements.

| | | |
|---|---|---|
| **Class 1** | Defines the lowest visibility level<br>Example: high-visibility trousers with two 5 cm reflective bands around each leg. These become Class 3 when worn with a Class 3 jacket | The colour of the background should normally be fluorescent yellow and the reflective material should comply with Table 5 of BS EN 471 |
| **Class 2** | Defines an intermediary visibility level<br>Example: vests with two 5 cm bands of reflective tape around body or one 5 cm band around body and braces to both shoulders | Colour scheme as Class 1 |
| **Class 3** | Defines the highest visibility level<br>Example: jacket with long sleeves, jacket and trouser suit with two 5 cm bands of reflective tape around the body, arms and braces over both shoulders | Colour scheme as Class 1<br>Must be worn on dual carriageway roads with a speed limit of 50 mph or above and must comply with the colour scheme to BS EN 471 |

**High-visibility garments and jackets with sleeves must comply with Class 3 and be worn when working on or near live high-speed roads.**

## 1.13.2 Other personal protective equipment

The wearing of other personal protective equipment (PPE) will invariably include safety footwear. Other PPE (such as hearing, eye and skin protection) must be worn when required due to the nature of the work being carried out. Safety footwear must have non-slip soles.

**The wearing of hearing protection is not a requirement when crossing live carriageways, because the risk of hearing damage from passing traffic is considered less than that of a person being struck by a vehicle because they were not fully aware of what was going on around them. A risk assessment would be required in these circumstances.**

## 1.14 Training

Although the New Roads and Street Works Act refers to a trained operative, there is no specific requirement in the Act for operatives or supervisors to undergo training or produce evidence of prior training.

However, the Act specifies the requirement for supervisors and operatives to hold suitable qualifications, except in prescribed circumstances. Furthermore, attention should be paid to the employer's duties as regards training as laid down in the Health and Safety at Work Act, the Management of Health and Safety at Work Regulations (as amended) and other relevant legislation.

## 1.14.1 National Highways Sector Scheme 12

National Highways Sector Schemes (NHSS) are bespoke, quality management systems for organisations working on the UK road network. There are currently more than 20 individual schemes, covering a range of highways-related activities (such as fencing, landscaping, road surfacing and marking).

There are several parts to NHSS 12, which covers temporary traffic management. Each part relates to different road types *(shown below)*.

| | |
|---|---|
| **12A/B** | High-speed motorways and dual carriageways. |
| **12C** | Mobile lane closures on motorways and other dual carriageways. |
| **12D** | Works on rural and urban roads. |

Any company that supplies services to the Highways Agency under the Specification for Highways Works (SHW) must be certified under all the relevant schemes for the work they will carry out. The schemes aim to make sure that work is carried out to the highest standards of professionalism, using properly trained staff. The scheme places a strong emphasis on health and safety qualifications under the various schemes, which are awarded by Lantra Awards.

F 01

# Appendix A – Signs and equipment

## Basic signs and equipment

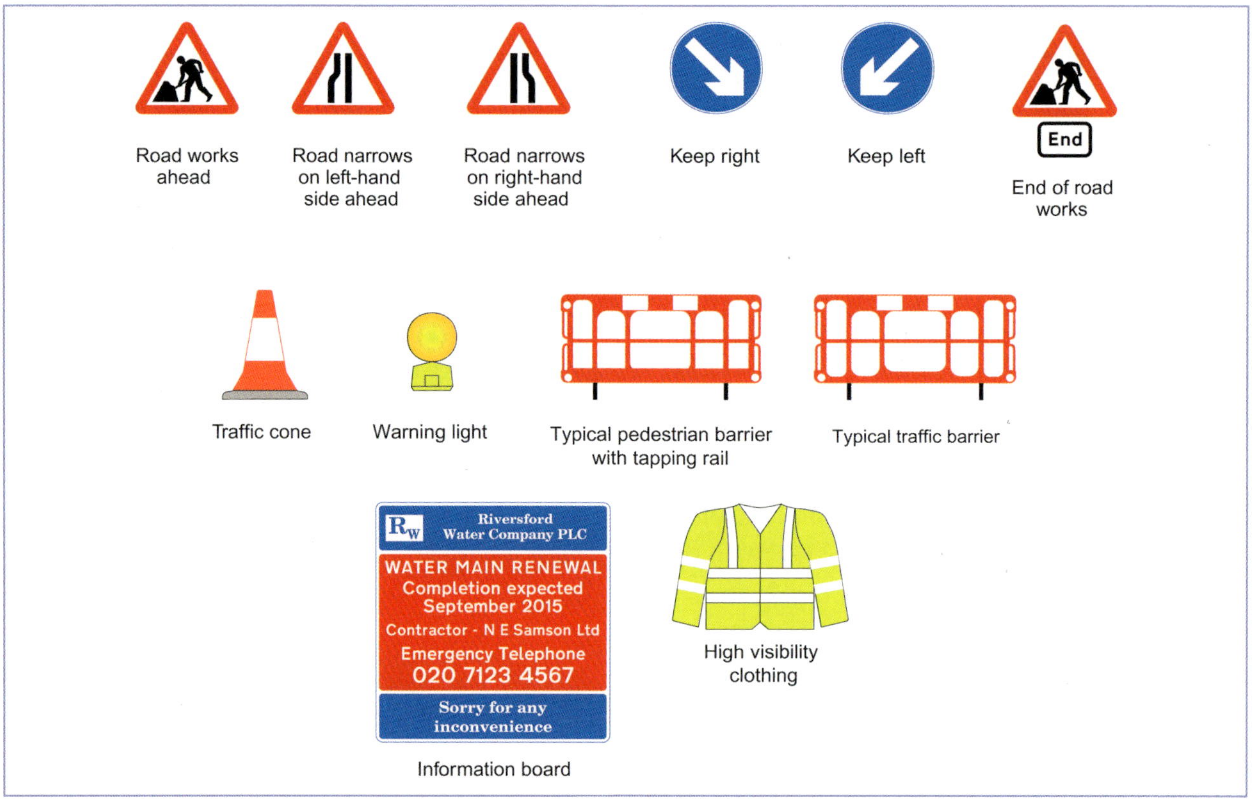


## Other signs and plates

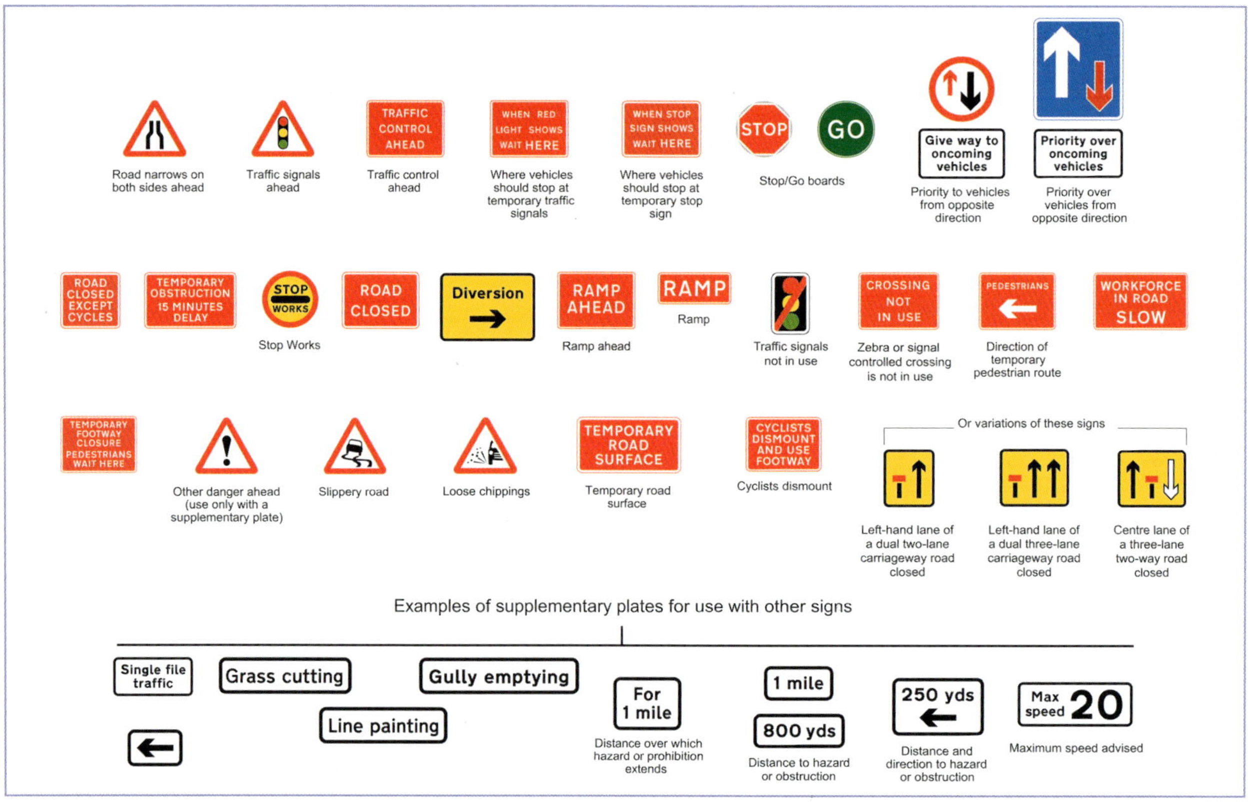


***Note:*** *this shows some of the more common signs in use. It does not show every sign that might be required.*

www.

**Based on © Crown copyright diagrams from *Safety at street works and road works – A Code of Practice 2013 edition*. For further information refer to the HSE website.**

# Appendix B – Traffic control

## Traffic control by give and take for roads with a speed limit of 30 mph or less

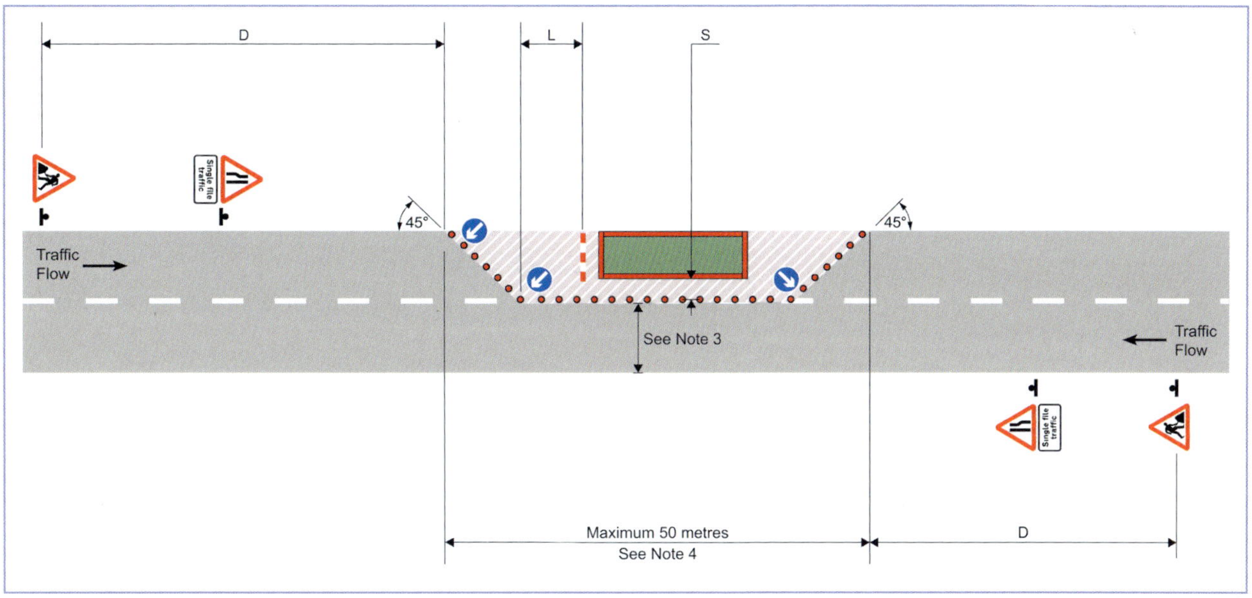


***Notes***

1. *For numbers and minimum size of cones, and dimensions D, L and S, refer to Appendix F.*
2. *An information board (omitted here for clarity) must be displayed.*
3. *Refer to page 52 of the CoP for guidance on unobstructed width past the works.*
4. *50 m maximum applies only where two-way flow cannot be maintained past the works.*

## Traffic control by priority signs

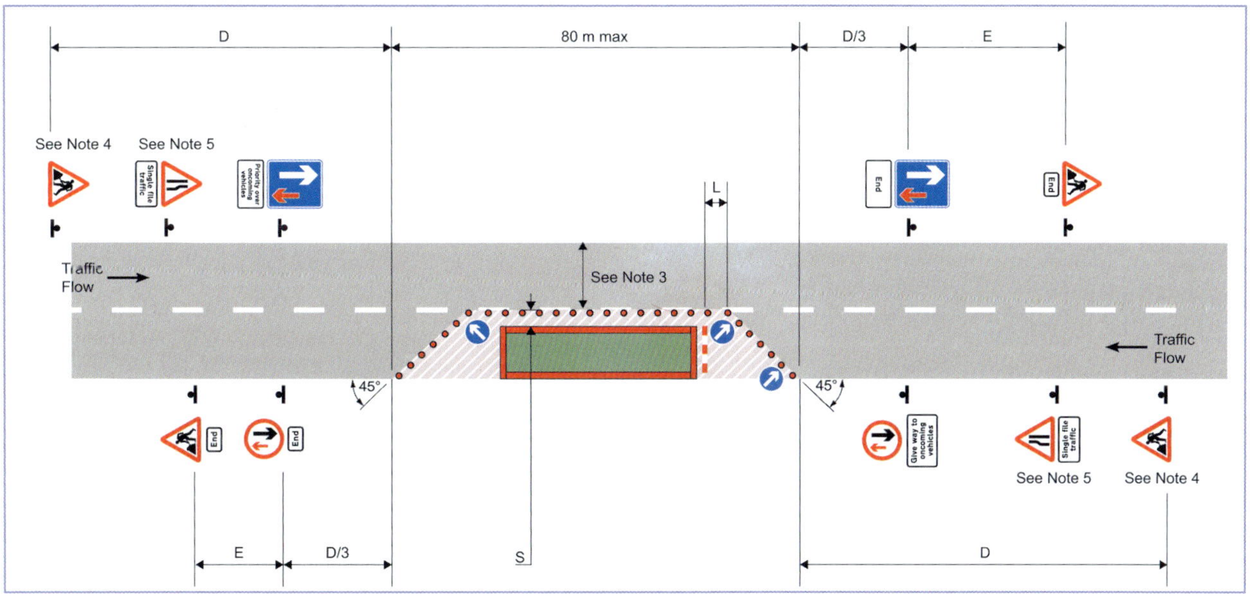


***Notes***

1. *For numbers and minimum size of cones, and dimensions D, L, S and E, refer to Appendix F.*
2. *An information board (omitted here for clarity) must be displayed.*
3. *Refer to page 52 of the CoP for guidance on unobstructed width past the works.*
4. *A supplementary distance plate is required for roads with a speed limit of 50 mph or more.*
5. *For roads with a speed limit of 50 mph or more an assessment should be made as to whether 'for' and a distance should be included on a supplementary plate.*

www.

**Based on © Crown copyright diagrams from *Safety at street works and road works – A Code of Practice 2013 edition*. For further information refer to the HSE website.**

## Traffic control by stop/go boards

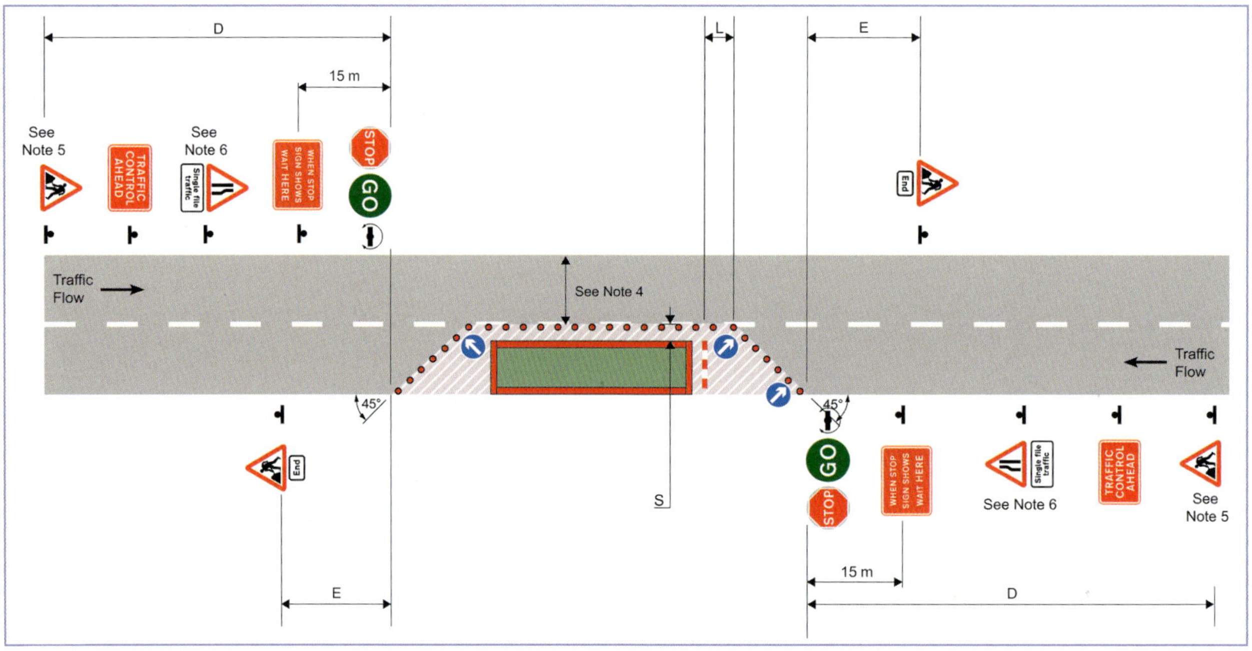


*Notes*

1. *For numbers and minimum size of cones, and dimensions D, L, S and E, refer to Appendix F.*
2. *An information board (omitted here for clarity) must be displayed.*
3. *Stop/go boards should be placed where they will be in full view of approaching drivers. They may be located on either side of the carriageway.*
4. *Refer to page 52 of the CoP for guidance on unobstructed width past the works.*
5. *A supplementary distance plate is required for roads with a speed limit of 50 mph or more.*
6. *For roads with a speed limit of 50 mph or more an assessment should be made as to whether 'for' and a distance should be included on a supplementary plate.*

## Traffic control by portable traffic signals

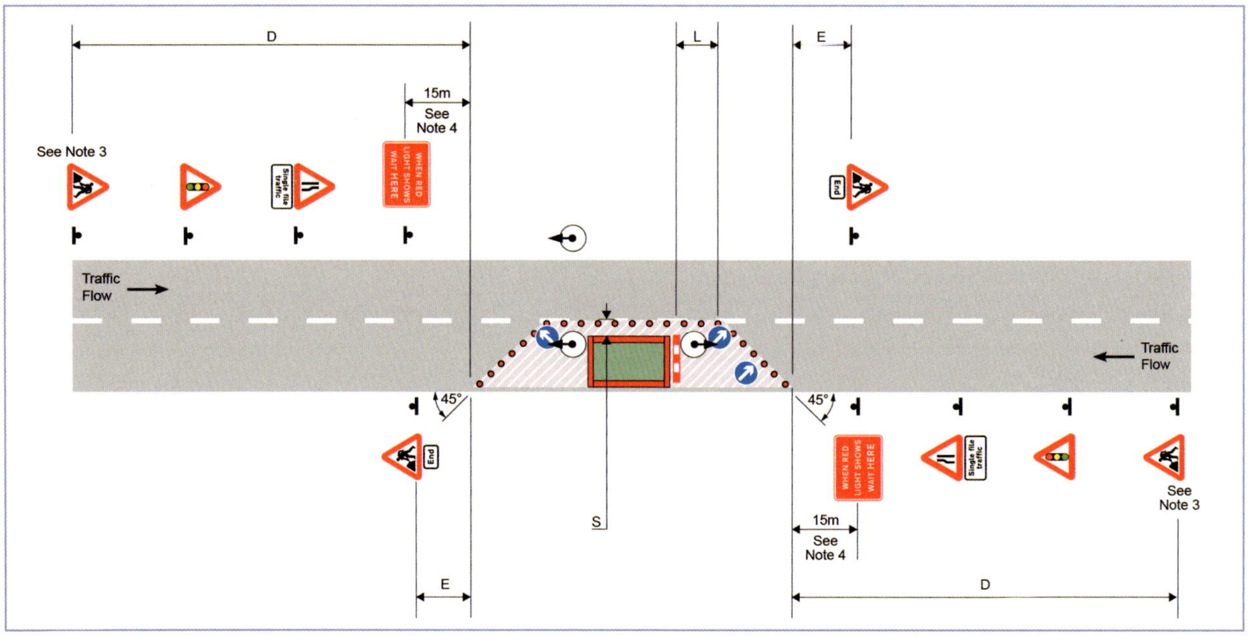


*Notes*

1. *For numbers and minimum size of cones, and dimensions D, L, S and E, refer to Appendix F.*
2. *An information board (omitted here for clarity) must be displayed.*
3. *A supplementary distance plate is required for roads with a permanent speed limit of 50 mph or more.*
4. *This distance may have to be increased in some cases to allow larger vehicles to pass the works.*

www.

**Based on © Crown copyright diagrams from *Safety at street works and road works – A Code of Practice 2013 edition*. For further information refer to the HSE website.**

# Appendix C – Works on footways

## Works entirely on the footway

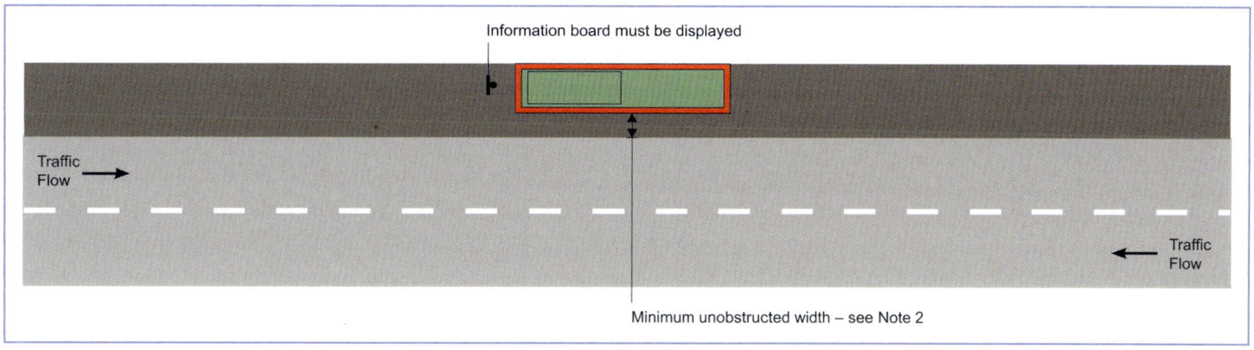


*Notes*

*1. Advance signs are not required when the works, signing, lighting and guidance are entirely on the footway.*

*2. 1.5 m preferred minimum unobstructed width, 1 m absolute minimum.*

## Works on footway with pedestrian diversion into carriageway

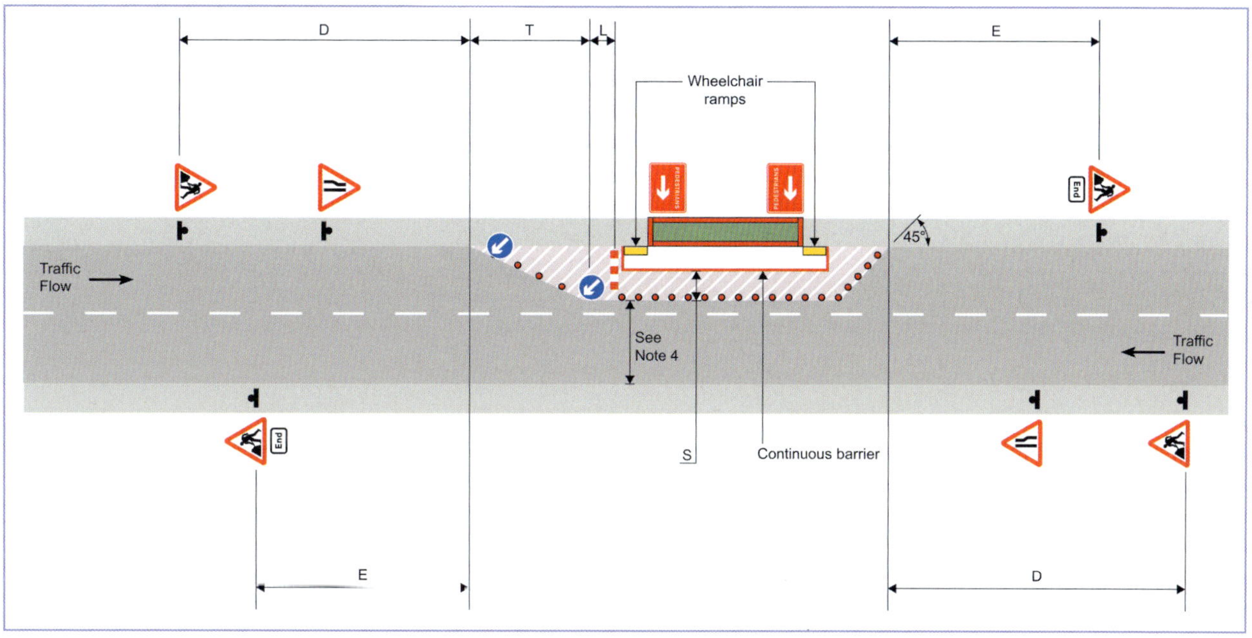


*Notes*

*1. For numbers and minimum size of cones, and dimensions D, T, L, S and E, refer to Appendix F.*

*2. An information board (omitted here for clarity) must be displayed.*

*3. Wheelchair ramps must be provided at the transition from footway to carriageway.*

*4. Refer to page 52 of the CoP for guidance on unobstructed width past the works.*

*5. Additional pedestrian barriers may be provided parallel or at right angles to the kerb, as site conditions require, to guide pedestrians past the works.*

www.

**Based on © Crown copyright diagrams from *Safety at street works and road works – A Code of Practice 2013 edition*. For further information refer to the HSE website.**

F 01

F 01

## Appendix D – Carriageway works

### Works between parked vehicles with a speed limit of 30 mph or less

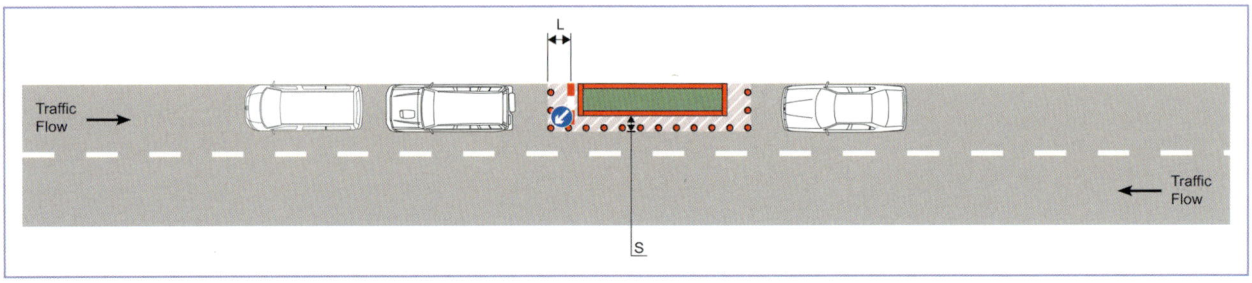


***Notes***

1. *No advance signing, lead-in taper or exit taper required provided that the whole works, including the safety zone, do not extend beyond the line of vehicles.*
2. *An information board (omitted here for clarity) must be displayed.*
3. *If parked vehicles move away, tapers and advance signing should be provided.*

### Works obstructing a signal controlled pedestrian crossing

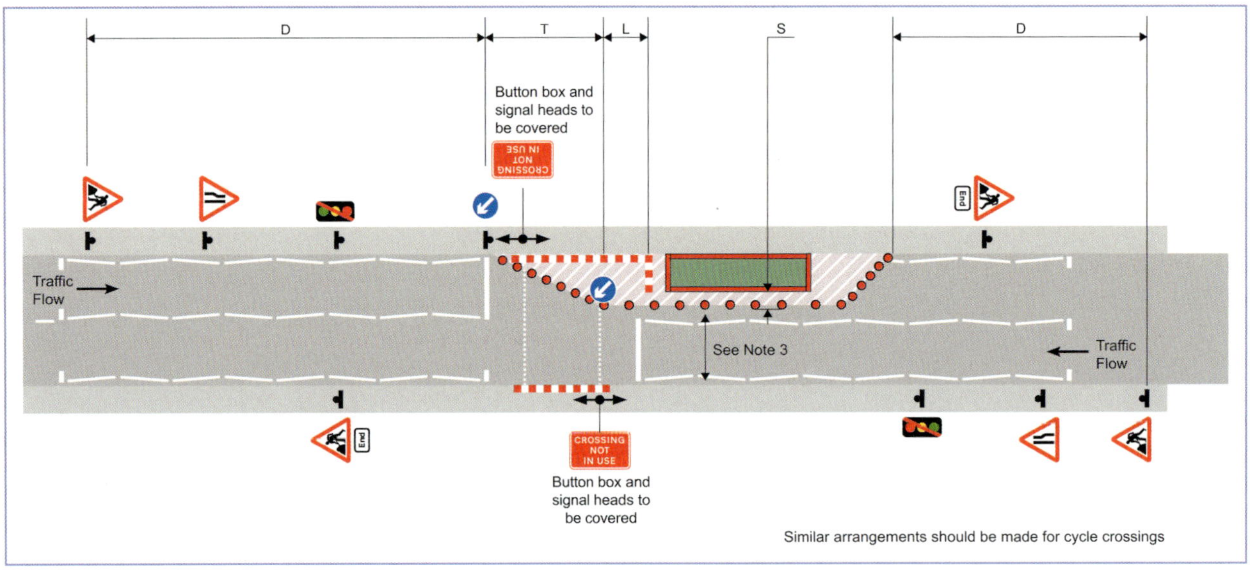


***Notes***

1. *For numbers and minimum size of cones, and dimensions D, T, L and S, refer to Appendix F.*
2. *An information board (omitted here for clarity) must be displayed.*
3. *Refer to page 52 of the CoP for further guidance on unobstructed width past the works.*

www.

**Based on © Crown copyright diagrams from *Safety at street works and road works – A Code of Practice 2013 edition*. For further information refer to the HSE website.**

# Appendix E – Mobile works

## Mobile works on a single carriageway road

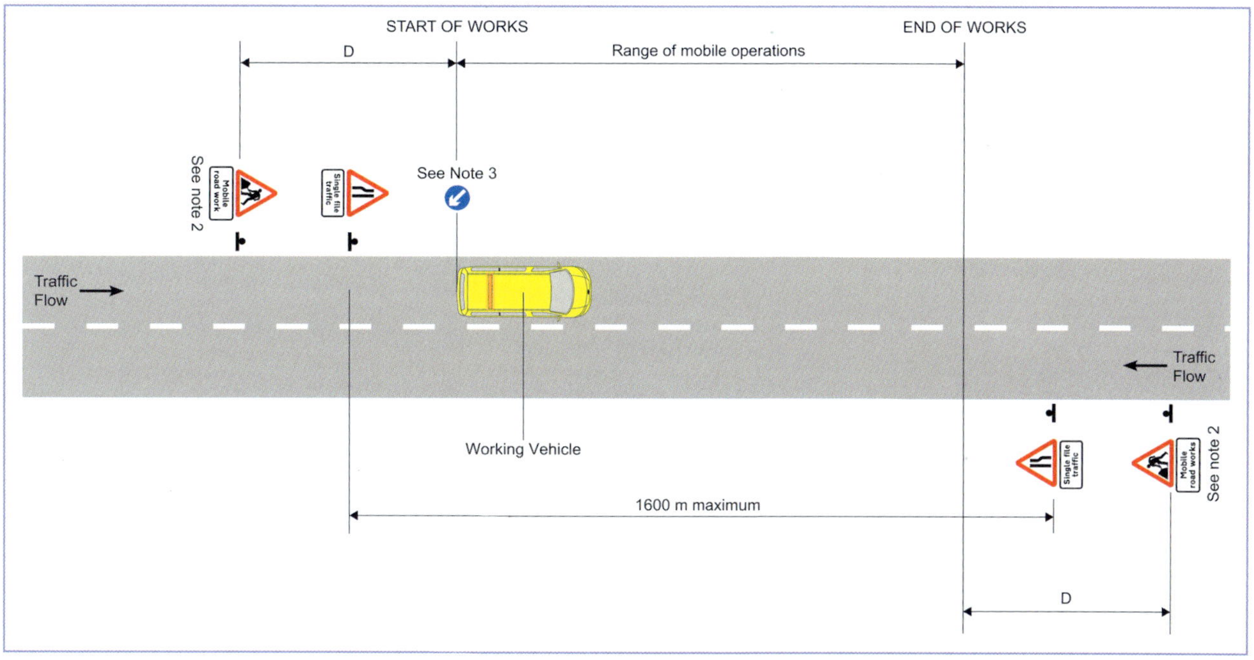


***Notes***

1. *For dimension D refer to Appendix F.*
2. *Or permitted variants.*
3. *Where a risk assessment determines that it is necessary to display signs on the working vehicle, they must comply with TSRGD (TSR (NI) in Northern Ireland).*

**Based on © Crown copyright diagrams from *Safety at street works and road works – A Code of Practice 2013 edition*. For further information refer to the HSE website.**

## Appendix F – Setting out site

(Distances in metres unless stated otherwise, numbers are minimum numbers)

| Type of road | Minimum visibility distance to first sign | D Distance from first sign to start of lead-in taper | Lead-in taper | Width of works including sideways safety zone 1m | 2m | 3m | 4m | 5m | 6m | 7m | S Minimum width of sideways safety zone | E Distance from last cone to End of works sign | Minimum size of signs (mm) |
|---|---|---|---|---|---|---|---|---|---|---|---|---|---|
| Single carriageway – speed limit 30 mph or less | 60 | 20 to 45 | T Taper length | 13 | 26 | 39 | 52 | 65 | 78 | 91 | 0.5 | 10 to 30 | 600 |
| | | | No of cones | 4 | 4 | 6 | 7 | 9 | 10 | 12 | | | |
| | | | No of lights | – | – | – | – | – | – | – | | | |
| Single carriageway – speed limit 40 mph | 60 | 45 to 110 | T Taper length | 20 | 40 | 60 | 80 | 100 | 120 | 140 | 0.5 | 30 to 45 | 750 |
| | | | No of cones | 4 | 6 | 8 | 10 | 13 | 15 | 17 | | | |
| | | | No of lights | 3 | 5 | 7 | 9 | 12 | 14 | 16 | | | |
| Single carriageway – speed limit 50 mph or more | 75 | 275 to 450 | T Taper length | 25 | 50 | 75 | 100 | 125 | 150 | 175 | 1.2 | 30 to 45 | 750 |
| | | | No of cones | 4 | 7 | 10 | 13 | 15 | 18 | 21 | | | |
| | | | No of llights | 3 | 6 | 9 | 12 | 14 | 17 | 20 | | | |
| All-purpose dual carriageway – speed limit 40 mph or less | 60 | 110 to 275 | T Taper length | 25 | 50 | 75 | 100 | 125 | 150 | 175 | 0.5 | 30 to 45 | 750 |
| | | | No of cones | 4 | 7 | 10 | 13 | 15 | 18 | 21 | | | |
| | | | No of lights | 3 | 6 | 9 | 12 | 14 | 17 | 20 | | | |

| Speed limit mph | 20 | 30 | 40 | 50 | 60 |
|---|---|---|---|---|---|
| L Longways clearance | 0.5 | 0.5 | 15 | 30 | 60 |

| Speed limit mph | 30 or less | 40 or more |
|---|---|---|
| C Clearance to works vehicle | 2 | 5 |

***Notes***

1. *For roads covered by this Code, the minimum height of cones is 450 mm where the speed limit is 40 mph or less, and 750 mm where the speed limit is 50 mph or more.*
2. *The maximum spacing between cones in longitudinal lengths shall be 9 metres, but no fewer than two cones shall be used in any length between tapers.*
3. *Lead-in tapers where two-way traffic control is used, and all exit tapers shall be at about 45° to the kerb line with cones spaced 1.2 metres apart maximum.*
4. *In certain circumstances on congested roads with speed limits of 30 mph or less, the lead-in taper may be reduced to 45° (see page 19 of the CoP).*
5. *The longways clearance (L) is the distance between the end of the lead-in taper and the first traffic barrier placed across the lane.*

www.

**Based on © Crown copyright diagrams from *Safety at street works and road works – A Code of Practice 2013 edition*. For further information refer to the HSE website.**

# 02
# Trackside safety

## Contents



## Supporting information

**GT 700 Toolbox talks**

## Overview

**Working on a railway is a high risk environment. Not only do you have the normal problems of construction work to contend with, you also have the hazard of trains moving in close proximity at high speeds. High speed 1 was introduced for the Eurostar trains, which are capable of speeds of up to 186 mph. Domestic passenger services may run at 140 mph on this route. H2H will enable line speeds in excess of 125 mph. There could also be overhead electricity lines at 25,000 volts AC or third and fourth rails carrying up to 750 volts DC.**

**Despite a gradual reduction in the number of rail accidents per million miles travelled, during recent years several major accidents, which were eventually attributed to defective work practices by contractors and in-house maintenance staff, served to bring the focus back to competency.**

**It is important to understand that this chapter is intended as a brief guide for site managers to provide awareness only. However, for those who may be required to work, or put people to work, on the rail network, a summary guide on developing the competence of staff at all levels has been provided.**

## 2.1 Introduction

Competence plays a very important role in controlling health and safety risks when working on an operational railway system. In the context of working on the railway system, controlling the risks to health and safety depends upon managing a complex mix of infrastructure, railway-specific rules, human factors and safety management systems.

Network Rail (which manage the railway infrastructure) has laid down procedures that have to be strictly followed by all people working on railways. While the following information will contribute to working safely on railways, it can only be a summary of this complex subject and it is recommended that readers contact Network Rail directly for more detailed information relating to individual projects.

With the decentralised management of the railways, the fear was that the safety of the railway would be jeopardised by the introduction of independent railway operators. To prevent this happening the Office of Rail Regulation (ORR) took overall responsibility for rail industry health and safety regulation in April 2006. At the same time new regulations were introduced in the form of the Railways and Other Guided Transport Systems (Safety) Regulations (ROGS).

The ROGS Regulations are administered and enforced by Her Majesty's Railway Inspectorate (HMRI) of the ORR.

www.

**An explanation of how ROGS apply to safety critical work is contained within ORR publication *Safety critical tasks – Clarification of ROGS Regulations requirements* (Railways safety publication 4).**

The Rail Safety and Standards Board (RSSB) is a not-for-profit company, owned and funded by major stakeholders in the railway industry. A part of RSSB's remit is to publish and update railway group standards, which govern the way that work is carried out on the railways, including the management of health and safety.

Under the leadership of RSSB the industry is embarking on an ambitious project to transform the content and presentation of the rules currently published in the *Rule book handbooks*, which are task based and cover subjects such as duties of the controller of site safety (COSS) taking a line blockage.

**The onus is on contractors who work on the railways to make sure that they are referring to the most recent edition of any reference material.**

**For further details on the RSSB guide on developing the competence of staff at all levels to work on the rail network refer to Appendix C.**

The primary purpose of the RSSB review is to revise the previous modular rule book with the aim of significantly rationalising its content and restructuring the document so that it is more accurately targeted at the skill sets of end-users and clearly aligned with operational principles.

The objectives of rationalisation and restructuring are explained below.

- ☑ Reduce rule-based errors, violations and misapplication.
- ☑ Enable end users to exercise greater judgement and discretion in resolving operational issues.
- ☑ Reduce the need for, and the costs of future rule changes.
- ☑ Support industry goals for competence management and performance improvement.

**Persons who work on the railways must achieve additional competencies when compared to those in conventional construction work.**

## 2.2 Important points

- ☑ Means of access to the work site must be stated in the work package plan/task briefing. The access point may consist of a cabin, which may be staffed for the duration of the work.
- ☑ In order to ensure that members of the public do not gain access to rail sites, all sites must be secured at the end of each working day and any security or safety-related incident must be reported through the safety management information system (SMIS), as detailed in Railway Group Standard GE/RT8047 – *Reporting of safety related information.*
- ☑ The site rules must be displayed in the access cabin; each member of staff is required to sign in and out from the site.
- ☑ The work site must be scanned using a cable avoidance tool (CAT) for underground services by a competent person prior to the work commencing. Any services identified are marked and, if possible, temporarily removed (signalling cables).
- ☑ The COSS must brief the workforce on the site safety rules prior to the work starting, and brief the incoming COSS at the shift changeover.
- ☑ Following the briefing, each member of staff must sign the COSS briefing form to confirm they have understood the brief.
- ☑ Lighting must be in accordance with the Network Rail *Safety 365* document, which, amongst many other things, details lux levels and permitted lighting systems.
- ☑ Personal protective equipment (PPE) must comply with relevant British Standards and Railway Group Standards; the requirements are different to those for general non-railway construction work.

**PPE requirements must comply with Network Rail's PPE policy.**

Network Rail has introduced lifesaving rules, which are at the heart of their safety vision – everyone home safe every day – and the result of their ongoing commitment to eliminate all injuries and fatalities within Network Rail and the rail industry.

www.

**For further information refer to the Network Rail website.**

## 2.3 Network Rail licensing

www.

**If making enquiries about becoming a building or civil supplier to Network Rail, a list of the main contacts can be found on the Network Rail website, or you can email them directly.**

When tendering for work on the railways, the contractor has to present a licence and a health and safety plan to Network Rail. These describe how the contractor will manage the safety implications. Subsequently, the performance of the contractor and their workforce is measured against these documents. It is essential therefore that contractor's staff working on a railway project must be made aware of the contents of the two documents, and supervisors must ensure that they adhere to the contents.

A contractor will require sponsorship from Network Rail regions to enable them to enter the licensing system. Applying for a licence is a demanding, time-consuming job and contractors who do not have significant in-house knowledge of work on the railway infrastructure are advised to obtain assistance from someone with experience of this type of work.

However, it is important that everyone involved understands that the main aim is to check the contractor's existing systems, either against the Network Rail procedure or to align the contractor's systems with those of Network Rail (not to invent new ones).

Where a licence has been submitted, but is being reviewed, Network Rail may issue a provisional licence, which will allow the contractor to bid for rail work.

Acceptance of a licence by Network Rail should lead to training for the staff responsible for its implementation. This is important because, whilst the document will contain the company's normal management systems, there will be a number of areas that are specific to rail work (such as drugs and alcohol procedures, competence management, accident reporting and medical requirements). Managers working on rail contracts must understand and implement these requirements.

### 2.3.1 Railway contractors certificate

The railway contractors certificate (RCC) will be required by companies who do not hold a principal contractor's licence but wish to employ and appoint safe work leaders. Holders of the RCC will be contracted directly to Network Rail, **not** the principal contractor.

## 2.4 Safety management

### 2.4.1 Safety management systems

Rail operators must obtain a **safety certificate** for operating trains, or a **safety authorisation** for infrastructure managers (which includes station managers).

The status of a safety certificate and a safety authorisation is the same, in that they allow access to the railway; however, their scope will be different. Safety certificates and safety authorisations have a maximum period of validity of five years.

There are various exemptions for the requirement to have either a safety certificate or authorisation. Some of these are shown below.

- ☑ Those operating only in engineering possessions.
- ☑ Those operating on non-mainline transport systems where the maximum permitted speed is 40 kph or less.
- ☑ Tramways.
- ☑ Railways in factories and most harbours.
- ☑ Railways within maintenance or goods depots or military establishments.

In order to obtain a safety certificate or safety authorisation the operator must implement a safety management system that includes the following.

- ☑ A statement of the safety policy.
- ☑ Targets for the maintenance and enhancement of safety and plans and procedures for reaching those targets.
- ☑ Procedures to meet relevant technical and operational standards or other requirements set out in national safety rules, for example:
  - procedures and methods for carrying out risk assessments and implementing risk control measures
  - provisions for training and maintenance of competency
  - arrangements for the provision of information relevant to safety
  - procedures and formats for the documentation of safety information
  - procedures to control the layout of and changes to vital safety information
  - procedures to ensure that accidents, incidents, near misses and other dangerous occurrences are reported, investigated and analysed and that necessary preventative measures are taken
  - provision of plans for action, alerts and information in the case of an emergency
  - provisions for internal auditing of the safety management system.

In practice, a train operating company, as a vehicle operator, or Network Rail, as an infrastructure manager, will stipulate safety conditions in accordance with their safety management systems that need to be complied with for a particular contract. These will be incorporated into the licensing arrangements (see below) and the health and safety plan for the project. However, if contractors operate trains or carry out infrastructure maintenance outside of possessions then the requirements for the safety certificate, authorisation and safety management system will apply.

### 2.4.2 Personal track safety scheme

If work on a railway entails working on or near the line, workers must have completed a personal track safety (PTS) course and be issued with, and be in possession of, a sentinel smartcard. This smartcard must be presented for authentication each time the worker goes on or near the line. Competency can be authenticated by a number of means, including swiping the card with a smartcard reader.

Before undergoing training for personal track safety, workers must be certified medically fit for work in a railway environment, and undergo screening for drugs and alcohol. The standards of medical fitness are laid down in Railway Group and Network Rail Standards.

www.

**Workers who successfully undergo PTS training receive a *Keypoints – Personal track safety* (PTS) health and safety booklet outlining safe working procedures and their responsibilities when working on the railways. A PDF copy of the booklet is available online.**

### 2.4.3 Competency and training in track safety supervision

The ORR, having taken over responsibility for health and safety on the railways (from the Health and Safety Executive (HSE) in 2006), introduced a competence management system (CMS), the structure of which is explained in the ORR publication *Developing and maintaining staff competence (Railway safety publication 1).*

The publication explains how the requirements for competence apply to contractors and their sub-contractors.

All work on or near the line must be supervised by a COSS who will set up a safe system of work for the group of workers they are responsible for. The COSS must stay with the group at all times until the work is completed or they have been relieved by another COSS.

The guidelines below outline what competencies are required to allow particular work to take place.

- ☑ Controller of site safety (COSS).
- ☑ Individual working alone (IWA).
- ☑ Protection controller (PC).

All the above competencies allow qualified workers to work alone, on or near the line.

## 2.4.4 Personal track safety

This competency allows qualified workers to walk on or near the line alone, to access or egress the site only – ensuring they do **not** work.

It also allows qualified workers to work on AC/DC line areas under the control of a COSS, providing the staff hold AC/DC competence and PTS on the sentinel database.

This competency is valid for two years. Upon successful completion of a new course and any additional modules, the online sentinel database will be updated. However, another card will not be issued. (The new sentinel smartcards replace the previous cards, which are no longer valid for access to Network Rail infrastructure.)

## 2.4.5 Lookout or site warden

This competency allows a qualified person to have:

- ☑ lookout duties in a red zone
- ☑ site warden duties in a green zone.

## 2.4.6 Person in charge of possession

This competency enables a person to carry out person in charge of possession (PICOP). This role is specific to Network Rail.

To be a PICOP (or engineering supervisor), details demonstrating COSS experience within the last 24 months must be held in the employer's competence management system. The PICOP will also be required to meet in full certain experience criteria.

PICOP competence itself does not qualify anyone to do COSS work, which requires a separate COSS qualification.

**For information on developing and maintaining staff competence refer to Appendix C.**

## 2.4.7 Safety critical work

The ROGS Regulations lay down a procedure to ensure that those engaged on a transport system in a work situation do so in a manner that will not affect the health and safety of people using that transport system.

All workers must be competent and fit to carry out their allotted tasks. They must also work in such a way that the number of hours worked, combined with the rest periods taken between work, does not increase the risk of fatigue to operatives.

It is obvious that any work carried out on the railway (whether to the track, the signalling system or the trains themselves) could have disastrous effects if it is not carried out correctly.

The whole reasoning behind the ROGS Regulations is to ensure that only competent persons carry out work on the railways. These regulations should ensure that the work will be carried out to such a high standard that the risk of disaster will be negligible.

## 2.4.8 Train movements

**A train travelling at 80 mph will cover nearly 120 feet (36 m) per second. If it takes 10 seconds to realise that a train is approaching and move off the track to a place of safety, in that time the train will have covered nearly 1,200 feet (360 m).**

When anyone is working on or near a railway line, the driver of an approaching train should blow the train whistle or horn to warn of the train's approach, although this must not be relied upon. The worker, in return, must acknowledge that they have heard the whistle, and have moved to a position of safety, by raising one arm straight in the air above their head.

The time required is decided by the COSS by conducting a risk assessment and will depend on the speed of the approaching train and the length of time necessary to remove staff and place tools away from the running lines to enable the whole group to be standing in a position of safety for at least 10 seconds before the train passes the worksite. The speed of the train is always taken as the maximum permissible speed at that location.

When setting up a safe system of work, a COSS needs to determine the distance at which they must be able to see a train approaching. The *Rule book* (GO/RT8000) defines safety distances as, if the maximum speed is:

- ☑ 100 mph or less, a person is in a position of safety if they are at least 1.25 m (4 feet) from the nearest line on which a train can approach
- ☑ over 100 mph, the distance increases to 2 m (6 feet 6 inches).

**A train sighting chart and an explanation of how it is used is included at Appendix A.**

## 2.4.9 Communications procedure

You must make sure you properly understand the meaning of all messages whether they are communicated by phone, radio or face-to-face.

- ☑ Make sure you are talking to the right person.
- ☑ Give your location, if using a phone or radio.
- ☑ Give your name and the name of your employer.
- ☑ State what task you are performing.
- ☑ If necessary, let the person know how you can be contacted.
- ☑ Use the phonetic alphabet to make sure names and locations that are difficult to pronounce are fully understood.
- ☑ Never use the words 'not clear' to describe a line that is obstructed; always use 'line blocked'.
- ☑ You must say numbers one at a time (for example, you should say 8107 as 'eight, one, zero, seven'). There are exceptions to this (such as when giving the time or when referring to a rule book module or handbook).

If you are receiving a message, make sure you fully understand it. You must repeat the message back so that the other person knows you correctly understand it.

Ensure the following to help make sure your message is fully understood when using a telephone or radio.

- ☑ Speak with the mouthpiece close to your mouth and speak directly into the mouthpiece.
- ☑ Talk slightly slower than normal using a natural rhythm.
- ☑ Use your normal level of volume when speaking.
- ☑ Avoid using hesitation sounds (for example 'um' and 'er').
- ☑ Use clear sentences.
- ☑ Get the person to repeat your message back to you.

During any conversation, one person must always take **lead responsibility**.

The person who must take lead responsibility depends on the task being carried out. Examples are shown below.

| Lead responsibility | When communicating with |
|---|---|
| **Electrical control operator** (ECO) | Anyone |
| **Signaller** | Anyone except the ECO |
| **PICOP** (person in charge of the possession) | Anyone except the ECO or signaller |
| **Route-setting agent** | Points operator |
| **Protection controller** (PC) | Each COSS |
| **COSS** | Members of the work group |
| **COSS** | Each lookout/site warden |

If it is not clear who has lead responsibility, or if two people carrying out the same task are communicating with each other, the person who begins the conversation must always take lead responsibility.

| Phrases to use when using a radio or telephone | |
|---|---|
| **Phrase** | **Meaning** |
| **This is an emergency call** | This message provides information that needs immediate action to prevent death, serious injury or damage |
| **Repeat back** | Repeat all of the message back to me |
| **Correction** | I have made a mistake and will now correct the word or phrase just said |

| Other phrases to use when using a radio and only one person can be heard at a time | |
|---|---|
| **Phrase** | **Meaning** |
| **Over** | I have finished my message and am expecting a reply |
| **Out** | I have finished my message, no reply is expected |

The **phonetic alphabet** must be used:

- ☑ to identify letters of the alphabet
- ☑ to spell words and place names that are difficult to say, or may be misunderstood
- ☑ if there is interference on the radio or phone
- ☑ when quoting the identity of signals or points
- ☑ when quoting train descriptions.

### The phonetic alphabet

| | | | |
|---|---|---|---|
| **A** – Alpha | **H** – Hotel | **O** – Oscar | **V** – Victor |
| **B** – Bravo | **I** – India | **P** – Papa | **W** – Whisky |
| **C** – Charlie | **J** – Juliet | **Q** – Quebec | **X** – X-ray |
| **D** – Delta | **K** – Kilo | **R** – Romeo | **Y** – Yankee |
| **E** – Echo | **L** – Lima | **S** – Sierra | **Z** – Zulu. |
| **F** – Foxtrot | **M** – Mike | **T** – Tango | |
| **G** – Golf | **N** – November | **U** – Uniform | |

## 2.5 Work sites

Work sites are categorised depending upon the degree of danger to the person(s) doing the work.

### 2.5.1 Possession of the line

When major engineering work is to be undertaken, a possession will be required.

This is an agreement with the signaller to give over control of the line, but control must be returned to the signaller when requested.

Possession of the line is taken by the PICOP from the signaller, and the PICOP is the only one who can allow trains in or out of the line(s) under possession. This procedure must be planned well in advance of the possession being required, otherwise it will not be granted.

Extra care is needed if one line is under possession and the line next to it is still open to train movements. Steps have to be taken to prevent people straying from the line under possession onto the open line.

### 2.5.2 Blockages of the line

Under this arrangement, trains are not permitted to run. The green zone may be created by various methods, one of which involves hand signallers using red flags to prevent the movement of vehicles past signals.

Extra care is needed if one line is blocked and the line next to it is still open to train movements. Steps have to be taken to prevent people straying from the line that is blocked onto the open line.

F
02

### 2.5.3 Considerations when undertaking track work

#### 2.5.3.1 Fencing and separation

To prevent people at a work site straying onto lines that are open to train movements, physical reminders can take the form of blue, one metre-high fencing, or black and yellow tape extending beyond the length of the work site. The fencing must be supported to prevent it being dragged under passing trains. An alternative type of fence is a Vortok rigid barrier.

Fencing acts as a continual reminder to people on site that, beyond the fencing, the track is open to movement of trains. Therefore, a safe system of work exists, providing no-one strays beyond the fencing (*refer to Figures 2, 3 and 4 in Appendix B*).

An alternative to fencing is to use site wardens to prevent people straying onto lines that are open to train movements.

The wardens are positioned by the COSS at least two metres away from the nearest rail of any line on which a train may run, to warn anyone who moves beyond that two metre point *(refer to Figure 5 in Appendix B).*

Employing this system as a means of warning depends upon the alertness of the site wardens ensuring their colleagues do not stray beyond the limits set by the COSS, within two metres of the open line.

#### 2.5.3.2 Prohibition of work

Where it is not possible to set up a green zone and work is not permitted in red zones, work must not be carried out on that site.

#### 2.5.3.3 Work planning

All work on or near the line must be planned by a safe system of work planner (SSOWP). The planner provides a safe system of work pack, which is issued to the COSS at least one shift prior to the planned work item. SSOWP is a sentinel competence.

The protection arrangements chosen must be the best available from the following list.

| | |
|---|---|
| **Best** | Safeguarded green zone |
| **2nd** | Fenced green zone |
| **3rd** | Separated green zone |
| **4th** | Red zone with automatic track warning system |
| **5th** | Red zone with train-operated warning system |
| **6th** | Red zone with lookout-operated warning system |
| **7th** | Red zone with lookout and portable warning system |
| **Last resort** | Red zone with lookout(s) only |

Together, these will lead to work that is better planned and co-ordinated to provide a higher level of safety. They will also help to drive further improvements through the introduction of systems that offer better protection and are simpler to use. These include T-CODs, ATWS and plans for a simplified version of T(ii) protection arrangement to make it easier to obtain green zones.

www.

**In some circumstances, all red zone working is banned or the use of lookouts is banned. More information can be found in the *National hazard directory* published by Network Rail.**

## 2.6 Safe working practices

### 2.6.1 Mobile plant

Any mobile plant used on the railways must not create a danger to the passage of trains. This entails the COSS setting up a safe system of work for the use of that plant within the work task to be carried out.

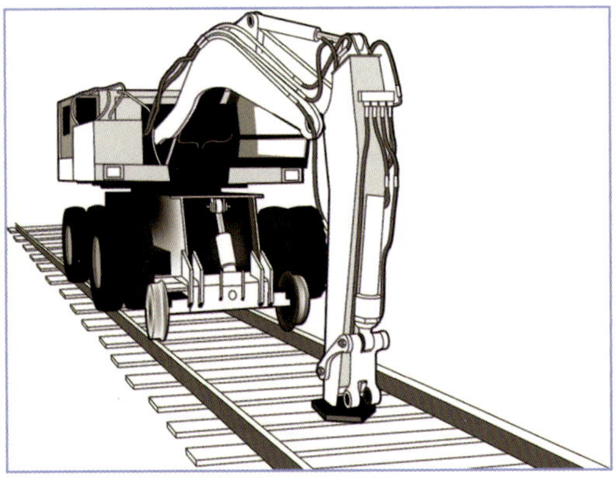

A work package plan and task briefing sheets should identify how plant will be brought to site, used on site and taken off site.

Some mobile plant is capable of being driven on both the road and on rails, as illustrated, and such plant must conform to the appropriate Railway Group Standard. Contractors using plant that can move on rails must be a plant operating scheme (POS) holder, not only as a contractor but also as a train operator, because the item of plant is classed as a train.

The method of getting the plant to and from site must be looked at very carefully. Contractors should ensure that the plant does not damage other vital equipment (such as structures, signalling equipment, including cables, and communications equipment).

Ways of protecting the various items of equipment must be clearly outlined in the work package plan and task briefing sheets for the work.

When working on site with mobile plant, various factors have to be taken into consideration, such as those shown below.

- ☑ The presence of electrified lines.
- ☑ The presence of underground services.
- ☑ The presence of signalling equipment.
- ☑ Working on embankments.
- ☑ Obstructing the sighting of signals from train drivers.
- ☑ The distance from running lines.
- ☑ The use of lights on road vehicles.

These are in addition to the normal precautions that have to be taken by plant operators in any working environment.

Where items of plant are used in relation to railway infrastructure, they must be used only by competent persons.

Certificates of competence to operate items of plant must be carried, along with means of identification. These credentials can be asked for at any time. Failure to provide them when requested will result in the person being removed from site.



## 2.6.2 Scaffolds and mobile towers

Scaffold work in a railway environment is a specialist activity, requiring the scaffolders to be competent not only in scaffolding but also in railway work.

A train requires clearance between itself and any structure that it passes. These clearances vary according to the train speed, the type of rolling stock, the presence or non-presence of curves and the cant of the track.

The required clearances need to be observed when erecting a scaffold or mobile tower to ensure that it cannot be struck by passing trains, and that the movement of air caused by trains passing does not affect the structure.

A thorough survey of the site must be made prior to the erection of any scaffold or mobile tower. The survey must consider the needs of railway personnel who need an unobstructed view of equipment in order to carry out their work safely.

Failure to carry out this survey correctly could have extremely serious effects.

Erection of scaffolds and mobile towers on the railway must be carried out, bearing in mind the following.

- ☑ Movement of trains.
- ☑ Movement of station staff and passengers.
- ☑ Proximity of electrified lines.
- ☑ Placing of other equipment used in operations.

It is vital that scaffolds or mobile towers are not erected in positions that will obstruct signals and other equipment that need to be seen by train drivers.

Special regulations exist for the erection and use of scaffolds or mobile towers, adjacent to or over the tracks, and these must be carried out in such a way that train movements are not affected.

When scaffolding has to be erected where electrified lines are situated, the method of erection, working and dismantling must take account of the hazards presented by the presence of the electrified lines.

The erection or dismantling of a scaffold or mobile tower must not commence until an isolation permit has been received to indicate that it is safe to work near the electrified lines. The need for isolation of electrified lines during scaffold erection and dismantling is of paramount importance to avoid contact with live lines when moving scaffold poles around. The stoppage of trains during this process should also be considered because of the possibility of the incomplete scaffold collapsing onto the track.

**Even if an electrical isolation permit has been received, it will not prevent the movement of non-electrified trains or runaway rolling stock.**

Signalling systems operate when the wheels and axles of a train running along the rails create an electrical connection of one rail to the other. This allows a small current to flow and operate signal lights, indicating that the train is in that section.

Extreme care must be taken when erecting or dismantling a scaffold or mobile tower over tracks. If scaffold poles fall, or are placed across rails, the signals may change. This will result in false signals being given to train drivers (for example, green lights instead of red or yellow ones), which could have very serious results.

## 2.6.3 Confined spaces

There are areas on a railway that may be classified as confined spaces. These include box girders, closed arches, culverts, station basements and inspection pits.

Having identified the work station as a confined space, the following questions should be asked.

- ☑ Is there any way of carrying out the work task without entering that space?
- ☑ If there is a need to enter that area, how long is it going to take for the work to be completed?

Any entry into a confined space for work purposes must be controlled by means of a permit to work scheme.

**For further information on working in a confined space refer to Chapter D09 Confined spaces.**

## 2.6.4 Lineside fencing

The boundary of railway property is protected by the erection of lineside fencing. Any work on this fencing must be carried out in a controlled way to prevent inadvertent or unauthorised access to the railway.

Some sections of fencing, due to the close proximity of electrified lines, should be connected together by bonding to earth. This will avoid the risk of electric shock to people coming into contact with the fence.

Renewal of fencing should be carried out in such a manner that the access created can be controlled by use of personnel or temporary fencing during periods.

Whenever the site has to be left unattended, the fencing must be left in such a state that access cannot be gained.

## 2.6.5 Lineside vegetation

Removal of lineside vegetation can be hazardous for those involved. Some hazards are shown below.

- ☑ The close proximity of electrified lines.
- ☑ Fire.
- ☑ The types of tool used.
- ☑ Discarded rubbish.
- ☑ Vermin infestation.
- ☑ Invasive or injurious plants (such as Japanese knotweed).

Removal of vegetation must be carried out in such a way that it does not come within 2.75 metres of overhead electrified power lines and does not cause an obstruction of the track. Consideration also needs to be given to the presence of sub-surface cables, as many of these have previously been cut during the removal of vegetation.

Vegetation must not be burnt, because of the risk of smoke obstructing a train driver's vision.

Tools used for vegetation clearance can present hazards of their own. Safe systems of work should be drawn up when tools such as chainsaws and flails are used.

Rubbish attracts vermin, which in turn can create the hazard of Weil's disease. There is also the hazard of discarded hypodermic syringes. These should be removed while taking every precaution against wounds from contaminated sharps. If you come into contact with an unprotected syringe, you should seek immediate medical advice.

## 2.6.6 Working on stations and platforms

Although passengers use station platforms regularly and feel safe doing so, when work is being carried out a platform can be just as dangerous as the open track.

Work on platforms and the station infrastructure can be in various guises, such as painting, billboard erection, maintenance work and installation work.

Whatever the work being carried out, the inherent risks are the same.

- ☑ Passage of trains.
- ☑ Presence of electrified tracks and overhead cables.
- ☑ Movement of station staff.
- ☑ Movement of passengers and their luggage.
- ☑ Risk of fire.

Work on stations and platforms should be planned in the same way as work on any other part of the railway system. This will ensure the health and safety of all concerned.

Consideration must be given to the following points whenever work is undertaken on stations or their platforms.

- ☑ Work must not be allowed to interfere with the normal operation of trains.
- ☑ Work must not be allowed to interfere with the normal operation of the station.
- ☑ Work must be carried out safely, bearing in mind the presence of electrified tracks and overhead cables.
- ☑ The use of flammable substances may create additional hazards.
- ☑ The way in which materials to be used on site will be transported and stored.

Over the years, work being carried out on stations and their platforms has resulted in fatal accidents. This has been due to the lack of proper planning, failure to isolate power supplies and lack of proper control.

A safety-conscious approach is now being adopted in the way that contracts are drawn up for tendering. It involves bringing into the contract the requirements of the Construction (Design and Management) Regulations, the Railways and Other Guided Transport Systems (Safety) Regulations and the various Railway Group Standards that govern the way in which people work in a railway environment.

Below are the golden rules to remember when working on station platforms.

- ☑ Beware of passing trains.
- ☑ Beware of electrified tracks and overhead cables.
- ☑ Do not obstruct a train driver's vision of signalling equipment.
- ☑ Do not obstruct passenger routes.
- ☑ Know the fire and other emergency procedures.

Working on platforms within four feet of the platform edge, when carrying out engineering or technical work, is classed as working on or near the line. People working there are required to hold a valid personal track safety certificate, unless a green zone has been established.

A system of creating a 'high street environment' can be accomplished if the work is not on or near the line.

This can be done by erecting a physical barrier or by appointing a site keeper who is responsible for preventing the work encroaching on the railway infrastructure.

## 2.7 Personal safety

**As far as moving trains are concerned, the best form of personal safety is for every person in the workforce to keep a lookout for themselves and for everyone else.**

### 2.7.1 Personal protective equipment

The main priority is that workers are easily seen, particularly by train drivers. Therefore, wearing high-visibility clothing is an important requirement. The clothing must conform to the requirements laid down by Network Rail and must be clean and worn correctly. However, train signals are in three colours: red, yellow and green, and so to reduce confusion to train drivers, there are colour restrictions for items of clothing worn by people working on or near a railway. Anything red, green or yellow must **not** be worn in case train drivers mistake them for signals.

The minimum PPE for the work site is shown below.

- ☑ High-visibility upper body clothing with reflective tape, which complies with BS EN 471:2003 Class 2 and Railway Group Standard GO/RT3279.
- ☑ High-visibility lower body clothing, which complies with BS EN 471.
- ☑ A safety helmet, which complies with BS EN 397:2012.
- ☑ Safety footwear, which complies with BS EN ISO 20345:2011, provides support to the ankle, includes mid-sole protection and has a protective non-conductive toecap.
- ☑ Other items of PPE as may be required to safely carry out specific tasks.

### 2.7.2 Working hours

Lord Justice Hidden at the Clapham Disaster Inquiry made several recommendations regarding the causes of accidents. One of his recommendations was that the hours of work should be controlled so as to prevent excessive times on duty.

As a result of these recommendations, the contractor must now prohibit excessive overtime working and shift lengths. Accordingly, personnel should:

- ☑ not work more than 13 turns of duty within any 14 consecutive days
- ☑ not work more than 72 hours within seven consecutive days
- ☑ have a minimum rest period of 12 hours between consecutive shifts
- ☑ not work more than 12 hours in any one shift.

Where a contractor is employed to work on signal and control systems or the renewal or maintenance of track, the requirements are enhanced to not more than 13 turns of duty to be worked in any 14-day period, and no more than 23 turns of duty to be worked in any two consecutive 14-day periods.

A contractor is required to keep records of the working hours of all staff working on railways, and these records must be kept available for inspection.

### 2.7.3 Drugs and alcohol

The Transport and Works Act stipulates the limits for alcohol consumption in the rail industry.

This legislation lays down the methods that must be adopted to ensure that anyone working on the railway is not under the influence of drugs or alcohol.

F
02

Personnel, both railway staff and contractors, working on a railway will be medically screened prior to employment for the presence of any of the following.

- ☑ Drugs, other than medication that does not affect their work performance.
- ☑ More than 29 milligrams of alcohol in 100 ml of blood.
- ☑ More than 13 micrograms of alcohol in 100 ml of breath.
- ☑ More than 39 milligrams of alcohol in 100 ml of urine.

Compare these figures to those laid down for driving a car.

- ☑ Not more than 80 milligrams of alcohol per 100 ml of blood.
- ☑ Not more than 35 micrograms of alcohol in 100 ml of breath.

It will be seen that far stricter controls are placed on those working on the railway infrastructure than on the ordinary driver.

There is a 'for cause' screening system for screening after a safety-critical incident has taken place. All personnel working on the railway must comply with screening.

Personnel found to register positive in any screening will be dismissed and could face prosecution under the Transport and Works Act for working under the influence of drugs or alcohol in a safety-critical work post.

## 2.8 Electrified lines

A large amount of the railway network is electrified, creating a hazard to anyone working in the vicinity of these sections.

There are three different types of electrified line.

- ☑ Alternating current (AC) overhead line systems.
- ☑ Direct current (DC) third rail systems.
- ☑ DC fourth rail systems.

### 2.8.1 AC overhead line system

An example of the typical components incorporated in an overhead line equipment system is shown in the following diagram.

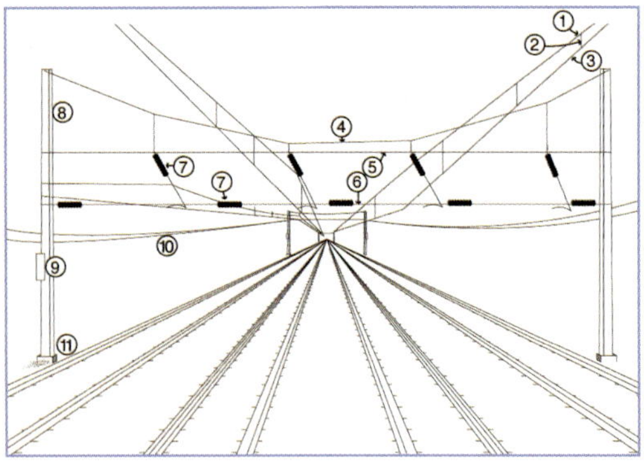

**Key**

| | | | |
|---|---|---|---|
| 1 | Contact wire | 7 | Insulators |
| 2 | Dropper | 8 | Headspan type structure |
| 3 | Contact wire | 9 | Structure number |
| 4 | Headspan wire | 10 | Return conductors |
| 5 | Cross span wires | 11 | Structure bond |
| 6 | Cross span wires | | |

In addition to the wires shown, bare-feeder wires supply electricity from trackside cabins. The overhead line equipment and attachments are electrified at up to 25,000 volts AC. Current is taken from the suspended contact wire by a pantograph on top of the train and passed through the train equipment to power the motors.

Take the following precautions when working on or near to overhead line equipment.

- ☑ Assume that the overhead line equipment is live at all times.
- ☑ Keep people, clothing, tools and equipment at least 2.75 m from:
  - anything attached to, or hanging from, the overhead line equipment
  - any broken or displaced wire connected to the overhead line equipment, whether hanging or lying on the ground.
- ☑ Take extra care not to come within 2.75 m of overhead line equipment in cuttings, or on embankments, structures or vehicles.
- ☑ Keep paint, water and other liquids well away from where they could be thrown, splashed or fall onto live overhead line equipment.
- ☑ Keep tools and equipment or ropes, wires, tapes and surveying equipment clear of live overhead line equipment.
- ☑ Keep pipes, rods, poles, brooms, mops or ladders horizontal when carried.
- ☑ Take special care when standing on the floor or load of open wagons if the overhead line equipment is live on the next line.
- ☑ Make sure there is no possibility of branches or debris coming within 2.75 m of live overhead line equipment when trimming or felling trees.

- ☑ Use ladders made of wood or approved non-conducting material. Do not use steel or aluminium ladders, or wooden ladders reinforced by metal attachments.
- ☑ When cutting water, gas or other metal pipe or metallic cable sheathing you must:
  – first connect a temporary electrical continuity jumper cable across the point where you will make the cut
  – keep the jumper cable in position until the pipe is again complete.

## 2.8.2 DC third rail system

Current passes through the third rail, which is raised **slightly above the height** of the running rails and is supported on insulators. The third rail is referred to as the conductor rail and is positively charged at 750 volts DC.

Current is picked up from the conductor rail by a pick-up shoe, situated on the outside of the train and passed through the train equipment down to the motors.

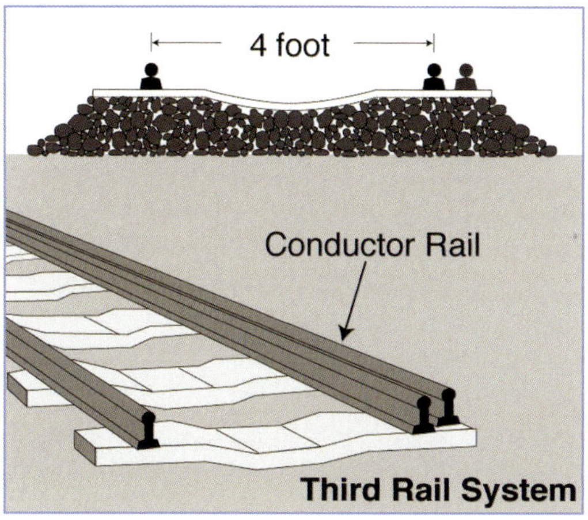


## 2.8.3 DC fourth rail system

On this system, current is returned to the supply by means of a fourth rail that is situated between the two running rails. The fourth rail, like the third, is mounted upon insulators and is slightly higher than the running rail and positively charged at 750 volts DC.

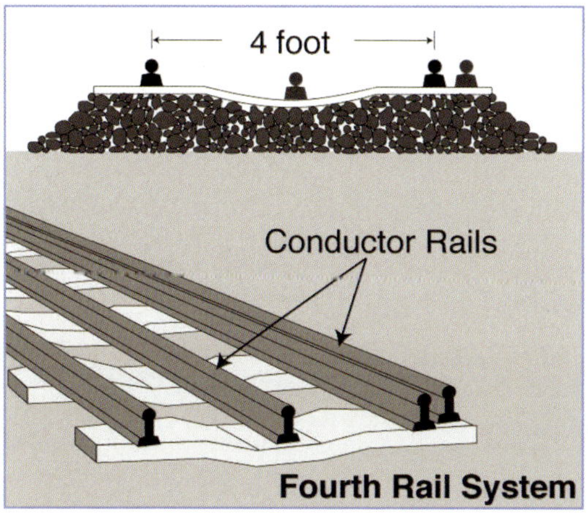


**Even if an electrical isolation permit has been received, it will not prevent the movement of non-electrified trains.**

### 2.8.3.1 Precautions before working on or near the line

Do not start work on, or close to, the conductor rail (or its connections) until it has been isolated.

The person requiring the isolation will be given a conductor rail permit. However, the issue of this permit does not mean that train movements are stopped on the lines concerned.

Do not work outside the limits shown in the conductor rail permit or those specified by your COSS.

The only exception is when special authority is given for certain types of work to be carried out without isolation. In such instances, precautions are specified that may include the use of approved insulated tools, insulated troughing, approved rubber mats or gloves. These must be in good condition and dry.

### 2.8.3.2 Precaution when adjacent to live conductor rails

- ☑ Keep paint, water and other liquids away from where they could be thrown, splashed or fall onto live conductor rails.
- ☑ Keep all tools and equipment or ropes, wires and surveying equipment clear of live conductor rails.
- ☑ Keep pipes, rods, poles, brooms, mops or ladders horizontal when carried, to avoid them accidentally touching the live conductor rails.

### 2.8.3.3 Precautions when working near DC lines

- ☑ Assume that the conductor rails are live at all times.
- ☑ Avoid crossing the tracks unless it is absolutely necessary, and whenever possible cross at a gap.
- ☑ Do not step on, touch or allow clothing, tools or equipment to come into contact with a conductor rail or any of its connections.
- ☑ Do not step on protection boarding or between a conductor rail and the adjacent running rail but, instead, step over those rails in one movement.
- ☑ Do not touch the collector shoes or their connections on any traction unit, whether or not in contact with the conductor rail.
- ☑ Do not step into flood water, which may be in contact with the conductor rail.
- ☑ If using a track circuit operating clip or device, apply it first to the rail furthest from the conductor rail.

# Appendix A – Train sighting chart

## Calculating the required sighting distance

e.g.

**The permissible speed at a location is 75 mph, and the work is of such a nature that the minimum warning time required is 30 seconds. Therefore, the sighting distance required is 1,050 m.**

However, not all lengths of track are straight and the view may be obstructed by bends, bridges or other structures. Therefore, it is essential for the COSS to assess these potential hazards as part of the risk assessment and by possibly appointing more than one lookout or alternative mechanical means operated by competent users in order to obtain the necessary sighting distance for an approaching train and to allow time for everyone to get into a position of safety at least 10 seconds before the arrival of the train. There will need to be a warning of the train's approach, which will be given by the site lookout.

Required sighting distances are calculated from the following chart.

## Sighting distance chart (metres)

**The warning time must be sufficient to enable everyone to be in a position of safety at least 10 seconds before the arrival of a train.**

| Permissible speed | Sighting distances to provide minimum warning time of: | | | | | | |
|---|---|---|---|---|---|---|---|
| (mph) | 15 sec | 20 sec | 25 sec | 30 sec | 35 sec | 40 sec | 45 sec |
| 125 | 900 | 1,200 | 1,400 | 1,700 | 2,000 | 2,300 | 2,600 |
| 120 | 900 | 1,100 | 1,400 | 1,550 | 1,900 | 2,200 | 2,500 |
| 115 | 800 | 1,100 | 1,300 | 1,550 | 1,800 | 2,100 | 2,400 |
| 110 | 800 | 1,000 | 1,300 | 1,500 | 1,800 | 2,000 | 2,300 |
| 105 | 800 | 1,000 | 1,200 | 1,450 | 1,700 | 1,900 | 2,200 |
| 100 | 700 | 900 | 1,200 | 1,350 | 1,600 | 1,800 | 2,050 |
| 95 | 650 | 850 | 1,100 | 1,300 | 1,500 | 1,700 | 1,950 |
| 90 | 650 | 850 | 1,050 | 1,250 | 1,450 | 1,700 | 1,850 |
| 85 | 600 | 800 | 950 | 1,150 | 1,350 | 1,600 | 1,750 |
| 80 | 550 | 750 | 900 | 1,100 | 1,300 | 1,500 | 1,650 |
| 75 | 550 | 700 | 850 | 1,050 | 1,200 | 1,400 | 1,550 |
| 70 | 500 | 650 | 800 | 950 | 1,100 | 1,300 | 1,450 |
| 65 | 450 | 600 | 750 | 900 | 1,050 | 1,200 | 1,350 |
| 60 | 450 | 550 | 700 | 850 | 950 | 1,100 | 1,250 |
| 55 | 400 | 500 | 650 | 750 | 900 | 1,000 | 1,150 |
| 50 | 340 | 500 | 600 | 680 | 800 | 900 | 1,050 |
| 45 | 320 | 420 | 520 | 620 | 720 | 820 | 920 |
| 40 | 280 | 360 | 460 | 540 | 640 | 720 | 820 |
| 35 | 240 | 320 | 400 | 480 | 560 | 640 | 720 |
| 30 | 220 | 280 | 340 | 420 | 480 | 540 | 620 |
| 25 | 180 | 240 | 280 | 340 | 400 | 460 | 520 |
| 20 | 140 | 180 | 240 | 280 | 320 | 360 | 420 |
| 15 | 120 | 160 | 180 | 220 | 240 | 280 | 320 |
| 10 | 80 | 100 | 120 | 140 | 160 | 180 | 220 |
| 5 | 40 | 60 | 60 | 80 | 80 | 100 | 120 |

If the work involves the use of noisy equipment, the noise produced may prevent the work team from being able to hear any warnings given by lookouts, a problem compounded by the requirement of wearing ear protection.

In such situations, a system of alerting the workers by the use of a touch lookout is implemented. This entails a lookout at the worksite to touch all the members of the work team to warn them of approaching trains.

## Appendix B – Fencing and separation

**The green zones are depicted by a hatched area, shown**

### Figure 1

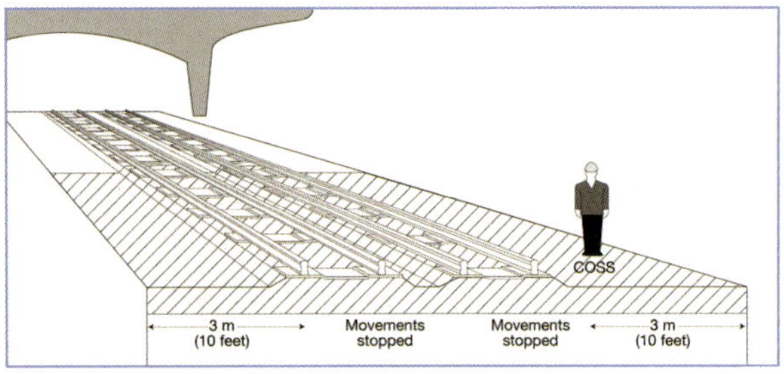


The diagram above shows a **safeguarded** green zone, with movements stopped on all lines.

### Figure 2

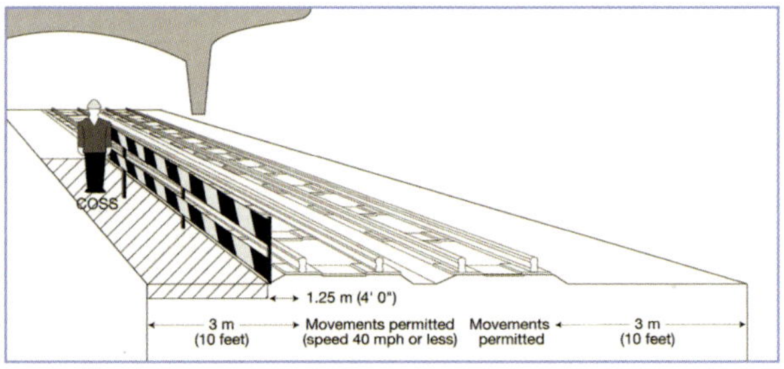


This diagram shows a **fenced** green zone using barricade tape or Netlon, with movements permitted on both lines but at a speed of 40 mph or less on the **adjacent line**.

### Figure 3

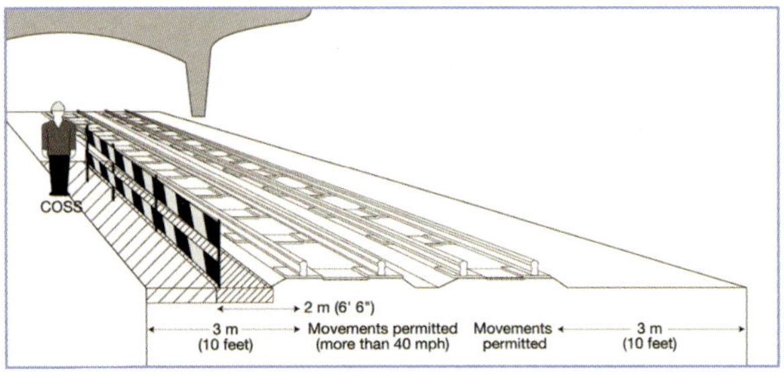


The diagram above shows a **fenced** green zone using barricade tape or Netlon, with movements permitted on both lines and at a speed of over 40 mph on the **adjacent line**.

### Figure 4

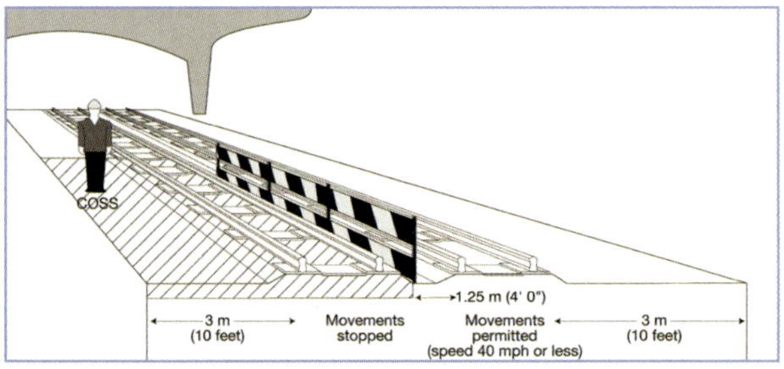


This diagram shows a **fenced** green zone using barricade tape or Netlon, with movements permitted on one line only at a speed of 40 mph or less.

### Figure 5

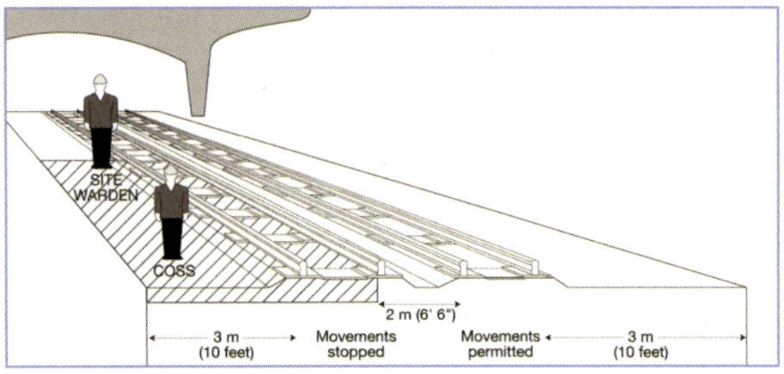


The diagram above shows a **separated** green zone, with movements permitted on one line only and where one or more site warden(s) has been appointed.

### Figure 6

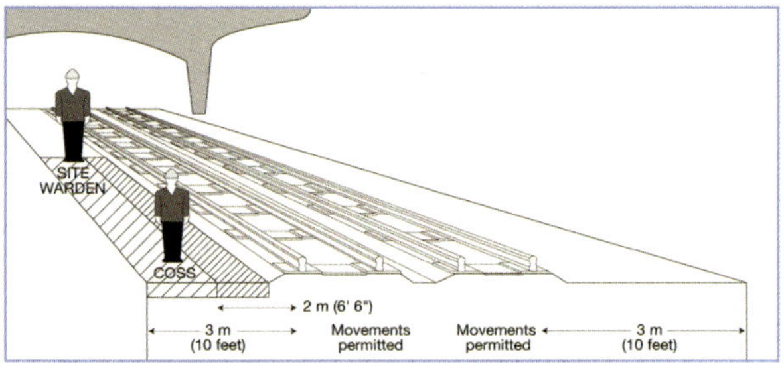


This diagram shows a **separated** green zone, with movements permitted on both lines and where one or more site warden(s) has been appointed.

# Appendix C – Good practice guide on competence development

## Purpose

The *Good practice guide* (GPG) *on competence development* represents a collation of previous RSSB good practice guides relating to training and competence, and reflects the latest developments and thinking around how to ensure staff competence.

It is designed to be used as a reference guide and a source of inspiration to help people working in the area of competence, allowing them to pick and choose ideas that are useful and practical, depending on their own requirements.

The GPG aims to move its users past the minimum standard as required by legislation – it is about going beyond the basics and providing you with the tools you need to develop comprehensive competence management systems as per your business and individual needs.

As understanding in the field of competence is always evolving, this is a live document that will be periodically reviewed and updated to reflect the latest thinking and resources relating to competence development.

## Target audience

Railway duty holders (infrastructure managers and railway undertakings) are required under the Railways and Other Guided Transport Systems (Safety) Regulations (ROGS) to make provisions within their Safety Management System (SMS) to ensure, so far as is reasonably practicable, that the competence of all safety-critical staff under their control is developed and maintained to a minimum safe standard.

This GPG has been developed to provide information and practical guidance to anyone who needs to understand, manage or contribute constructively to the analysis, design, delivery, review or assessment of training and other competence management activities.

The core text of this GPG is relevant to anyone with an interest in competence development (including the learners themselves), whereas the appendices are for more specific audiences (such as those with a more detailed interest in simulators, assessments, etc.).

## Scope

This guide is designed to act as a reference manual. It pulls together:

- ☑ the **evidence-based findings** of recent research projects, highlighting **practical guidance** rather than focusing on the academic theory behind them
- ☑ the content of the **previous five RSSB good practice guides** in the area RS/220; *Good practice in training* (RS/220)*, *Good practice guide to train driver training* (RS/221)*, *Good practice on simulation as a tool for training and assessment* (RS/501)*, *Good practice guide on competence review and assessment* (RS/701) and *Good practice guide for driver assessment* (RS/702)
- ☑ **details of technology** or other relevant mediums that support the implementation of innovative concepts
- ☑ a variety of small and more in-depth **case studies** (these provide real-life demonstrations to highlight good practice in the various areas, illustrating how different companies have adopted approaches that suit their learners and business)
- ☑ **links and signposts** to practical tools and further information.

The advice in this GPG mainly pertains to the competence of safety-critical staff, though many of the principles are widely applicable in the field of learning and development and will have relevance to other roles. Although the overriding objective of competence management is mitigation of safety risk, it should be borne in mind that safety risk is one component of overall business risk.

*This good practice guide is not a mandated document, even though it sits in the suite of Railway Group Standards (RGS) documents.*

www.

**For further details, the structure and full text of the *Good practice guide on competence development* refer to the Railway Group Standards Online website.**

*(The above text is extracted from the Good Practice Guide on Competence Development, Document no. RS/100, Issue 1, March 2013. This document is copyrighted and has been reproduced with the permission of the Rail Safety and Standards Board Ltd.)*

F
02

# 03
# Demolition

## Contents



## Supporting information

### GT 700 Toolbox talks

## Overview

**Demolition can be a hazardous activity. It is of a technical nature and should only be carried out by appropriately trained and supervised competent personnel.**

**This chapter gives an understanding of the potential problems associated with demolition, the good practices that must be followed and the criteria to appoint competent demolition contractors.**



## 3.1 Introduction

Safe demolition is a complex process, requiring a high level of technical skill. It is also potentially very hazardous if carried out by contractors who are not experienced and competent in demolition planning, management and delivery.

The word *demolition* is often misconstrued to mean large-scale, or to involve the complete removal of a structure or building. However, the removal of a single element of construction or the partial removal of a structure or building also constitutes demolition.

Information, planning, responsible implementation and controls are the essential elements for safe and successful demolition projects.

Whether demolition is required for a small building or structure, or for a complex industrial, commercial or residential site, you must be aware of the hazards and risks. These need to be identified, assessed and effectively controlled to avoid danger and remove or reduce the potential for injury to persons and damage to adjacent property, as far as is reasonably practicable.

A systematic approach to the demolition process starts with responsible clients making suitable arrangements for managing a project, including making sure duty holders are appointed and sufficient time and resources are allocated. Inexperienced clients may well need to seek the assistance of a demolition engineer or consultant for guidance in the appointment of duty holders and management of the demolition process.

- ☑ Demolition works should be planned in such a way that they are undertaken using systems of work that take into consideration safety, health, the environment, cost and efficiency.
- ☑ All those involved, from concept, through tender, to contract delivery, should ensure effective planning and communication, through the provision of sufficient time resource to facilitate effective planning and delivery of a successful and efficient project.
- ☑ Appropriate timescales required for the acquisition of any utility service disconnections, licences or permits should be allowed for in the pre-start programme of works.
- ☑ After the contract has been awarded, and before work commences, the demolition contractor should determine the proposed safe sequence of operations on the basis of an assessment of the comparative risks, related specifically to the site and local conditions.
- ☑ This sequence should be used to develop the construction phase plan (CPP) from the tender stage plan and detailed operational programme of works.
- ☑ The expanded tender stage plan should form the basis of the CPP (demolition plan) for the demolition.
- ☑ Management plans for waste should also be developed.
- ☑ The methods of work should allow for demolition work and site clearance, as stipulated by the contract, taking account of any constraints imposed by the client or local conditions.
- ☑ Adequate time should be allowed for setting up the site prior to work commencing and for delivering the works.

## 3.2 Important points

- ☑ Demolition can be hazardous and should only be entrusted to experienced contractors who employ well-trained, competent personnel. Many demolition projects, particularly within buildings constructed prior to 1999 (especially between 1960 and 1990) may contain asbestos.
- ☑ Recognise that structural refurbishment may involve demolition work and plan accordingly.
- ☑ Planning and supervision is vital to ensure a successful project.
- ☑ Demolition should be carried out with due regard to the British Standard (BS 6187:2011), good practice current at the time the works are being carried out, Health and Safety Executive (HSE) and industry guidance, and in full compliance with regulations.
- ☑ Ensure that prior to all demolition a site-specific refurbishment or demolition asbestos survey, as defined in the HSE publication *Asbestos: the survey guide* (HSG264), has been carried out by a competent person and that the information is available to those who need it.
- ☑ It should be noted that wherever paintwork or coatings are likely to be damaged or disturbed, the HSE advises lead (paint) surveys are carried out regardless of the age of the building or the extent of the works.
- ☑ **The Construction (Design and Management) Regulations apply to all demolition and dismantling projects**, regardless of size, but not all projects will be notifiable to the HSE.
- ☑ Ensure the works are properly planned with written risk assessments and method statements developed, communicated to the personnel carrying out and supervising the work and understood by all concerned.

- ☑ Managers should ascertain the stability of the structure due for demolition. Where there are any doubts or concerns, the services of a demolition engineer and/or structural engineer should be engaged.
- ☑ The removal of non-structural fixtures, fittings and finishes, often referred to as soft stripping, must be planned and controlled to avoid the risk of personal injury, uncontrolled release of asbestos, falling objects and so on.
- ☑ Demolition arisings should follow the hierarchy of waste minimisation (for example, reuse, reclaim and recycle) with waste being handled, managed and disposed of in accordance with current legislation and good practice.
- ☑ If processing and disposing of materials arising from the demolition (such as screening or crushing) ensure the relevant licences, permits or exemptions are in place.
- ☑ Ensure the waste duty of care documentation is obtained, completed correctly and records kept.
- ☑ A waste minimisation management plan should be developed and kept up to date, including records of all demolition waste streams and the quantities.



### Code of Practice for full and partial demolition (BS 6187:2011)

This Code of Practice takes the form of guidance and recommendations. The standard has been revised to reflect advances in technology and equipment in the demolition industry, and to give recommendations on the following principal areas:

- ☑ project development and management, site assessments, risk assessments, decommissioning procedures, environmental provisions and façade retention
- ☑ deconstruction techniques, including activities for reuse and recycling
- ☑ exclusion zones and safe working spaces, including their design and application.

Recommendations for methods of, and techniques for, demolition and partial demolition, including for structural refurbishment, have been retained, with consideration of specific types of structure, but the text has been significantly updated to reflect current and developing good practices. By being less prescriptive, this edition also allows for innovative techniques and methods to be employed.

## 3.3 Legislative requirements

### 3.3.1 The Building Act

Section 80 of the Act requires persons intending to carry out the demolition of a structure, or part-structure greater than 1,750 cubic feet (approximately 50 m$^3$), to give six weeks' notice to the Local Authority Building Control Department, which may incur an administration fee. A Section 81/82 counter notice is usually issued, providing conditions that apply to the works or a refusal with reasons.

This is normally something that the client or design team should have carried out, but it frequently falls to the demolition contractor.

### 3.3.2 Construction (Design and Management) Regulations

**Readers are advised:**

- ☑ **to refer to the industry guidance that supports the Construction (Design and Management) Regulations (CDM)**
- ☑ **that under these regulations the definition of construction includes demolition and dismantling, and is to be regarded as such when used in the following text.**

CDM applies to all construction, which includes demolition and dismantling work, as defined in BS 6187, regardless of the project's size or duration. A construction phase plan must be developed for all construction projects. The work will be notifiable to the HSE if the thresholds are exceeded. A principal designer (PD) and principal contractor (PC) must be appointed where more than one contractor is engaged.

A project is notifiable if the construction work on a construction site is scheduled to last longer than 30 working days and have more than 20 workers working simultaneously at any point in the contract, or exceed 500 person days.

To ensure site safety during demolition the principal contractor must ensure that one or more competent person(s) are appointed to plan and supervise the work. The level of supervision required will depend upon the risks to health and safety and the skills, knowledge, training and experience of the workers (for example, workers will require closer supervision if they are young, inexperienced or starting a new work activity). Other factors to consider are the levels of the individuals' safety awareness, education, physical agility, literacy and attitude. Any duty holder who puts another person to work on a construction site (for example, a principal contractor engaging the services of a demolition contractor) must ensure that the person is competent to do what is required of them.

F 03

If there is only one contractor on site (the demolition contractor), the responsibility for health and safety will rest with them. For all construction projects the client has to ensure that they have supplied adequate pre-construction information and that there are adequate welfare arrangements in place. As a reminder, a construction phase plan is required for non-notifiable projects.

The National Federation of Demolition Contractors (NFDC) and the Institute of Demolition Engineers (IDE) can provide information regarding the competence required for particular projects.

### 3.3.2.1 Stability of structures

- ☑ All practicable steps shall be taken, where necessary, to prevent danger to any persons, to ensure that any new or existing structure or any part of such structure that may become unstable or in a temporary state of weakness or instability, due to carrying out of construction work, does not collapse.
- ☑ Any buttress, temporary support or temporary structure must be of such design and so installed and maintained as to withstand any foreseeable loads that may be imposed on it, and must only be used for the purposes for which it is so designed, installed and maintained.
- ☑ No part of a structure shall be so loaded as to render it unsafe to any person.

**For further information refer to Chapter C04 Temporary works, and to the Code of Practice for temporary works procedures and the permissible stress design of falsework (BS 5975).**

### 3.3.2.2 Demolition or dismantling

The demolition or dismantling of a structure or part of a structure shall be planned and executed to reduce risk to as low a level as is reasonably practicable.

The arrangements for carrying out demolition or dismantling work shall be recorded in writing, prior to the commencement of the work.

### 3.3.2.3 CDM duty holders

The **client** is responsible for the provision of pre-construction information, which is already in their possession or is reasonably obtainable by them (such as the results of any refurbishment or demolition asbestos survey and the location and status of utility services). The client must also ensure the following.

- ☑ The project is notified to the HSE, if it meets that criteria.
- ☑ That adequate welfare facilities are provided.
- ☑ Relevant parts of the pre-construction information are distributed to contractors and designers to enable them to tender for, or prepare to carry out, the work.
- ☑ Suitable arrangements are made for managing the project so that health, safety and welfare are secured.

The client sets the tone for the intended demolition and, as such, care should be taken to ensure sufficient time and resources are made available to properly plan, procure and carry out the works.

The **principal designer** must plan, manage, monitor and co-ordinate the work of the pre-construction phase. They must liaise with the principal contractor in providing relevant information for the planning and monitoring of the construction phase. Principal designers may also be designers. Design work may include any structural work and temporary works design.

For notifiable works, the principal designer is responsible for the co-ordination of health and safety design and planning aspects for notifiable projects, including those below.

- ☑ Co-ordinate matters relating to health and safety during the pre-construction phase.
- ☑ Estimate the period of time required to complete work stages.
- ☑ Take account of general principles of prevention.
- ☑ Identify, eliminate or control foreseeable risks to health and safety of any person carrying out construction work, maintaining or cleaning a structure and/or using a structure designed as a workplace.
- ☑ Ensure designers comply with their duties.
- ☑ Ensure all persons co-operate with the client, principal designer and each other.
- ☑ Assist the client in the provision of the pre-construction information.
- ☑ Provide pre-construction information promptly and in a convenient form to every designer or contractor.
- ☑ Liaise with the principal contractor and share information relevant to the planning, management and monitoring of the construction phase and the co-ordination of health and safety during construction.

The minimum lead times for the project must form part of the pre-construction information. Principal designers must themselves be competent; demolition and asbestos issues may be too specialist for many who normally perform the principal designer's role and they should be prepared to take specialist advice, if required.

Depending on the number of contractors on site, the **principal contractor** or the **contractor** is responsible for the overall construction phase, taking into account health and safety issues and the development of the health and safety plan.

**Contractors** and other workers must all work together as a team to achieve high standards in health, safety and welfare on site. The contractors, which normally include utility companies, must co-operate with the principal contractor by obeying site rules and complying with relevant parts of the construction phase plan.

Regardless of the size of the contract, the client has to ensure there are suitable management arrangements for the project welfare facilities and allow sufficient time and resource for all stages. A written **health and safety plan** would be required for all demolition projects. The plan should be written by the contractor and include training and information for workers.

The **demolition contractor** may be appointed as the principal contractor subject to having the necessary expertise and understanding to undertake the role.

Irrespective of the size of the project, the demolition contractor must ensure the work is properly planned and carried out safely with the arrangements recorded (risk assessment, method statements, programme and so on). They must also ensure these arrangements are communicated and clearly understood by those carrying out the work.

**For general definitions and terms used by the demolition industry refer to Appendix A.**

## 3.4 Project documents

### 3.4.1 Demolition plan

All demolition, and partial demolition, work should be planned and carried out in such a way as to remove or reduce the risks to people to as low as reasonably practicable.

**The arrangements for carrying out such demolition, or partial demolition, should be recorded in writing before the demolition work begins, with a level of detail proportionate to the risks involved. The demolition plan should form part of the construction phase plan.**

### 3.4.2 Construction phase plan

The construction phase plan (often referred to as the health and safety plan) provides a focus for the construction phase of a project.

Relevant pre-construction information, relating to the health and safety hazards associated with the work, should be provided by the client regardless of the size of the project. If the project is notifiable, the principal designer must carry out the tasks outlined previously, with regard to the collection and distribution of the pre-construction information.

In the context of this chapter, such information is likely to include:

- ☑ the location and physical condition of any asbestos where its presence has been identified by a refurbishment/demolition asbestos survey, as defined in HSG264
- ☑ the results of structural surveys
- ☑ notices, acknowledgements and disconnection certificates received for all services

- ☑ plans identifying the location of underground services
- ☑ the possible presence of contaminants, for example:
  - polychlorinated biphenyls (PCBs) in old electrical transformers
  - the residual contents of tanks and pipelines
  - the location and nature of contaminated ground
- ☑ any other information that is required to ensure that the work can be planned safely and would not reasonably be expected to be known by a competent contractor.

After being appointed by the client, the principal contractor must use the pre-construction information provided by the client to develop the construction phase plan to the satisfaction of the client.

The health and safety plan must be:

- ☑ sufficiently developed prior to any work commencing on site
- ☑ reviewed and amended as often as is necessary for the duration of the project
- ☑ communicated to those on the site insofar as it is necessary for any person to be aware of any part of it.



### 3.4.3 Risk assessment

The following principles of risk assessment should be followed when determining methods and sequences of work.

- ☑ Identify the hazards associated with the proposed work.
- ☑ Consider who might be harmed and how, including workers, site visitors, members of the public and anyone affected by the work.
- ☑ Evaluate the risks and identify the precautions required by, for example, comparison with good practice and categorisation of risk level (likelihood and severity).
- ☑ Record the findings and implement the control measures for the residual risks.
- ☑ Review the risk assessment and update if necessary.

The risk assessment should take into account any constraints that the client has identified, but the demolition contractor should be given the freedom to determine the proposed methods of demolition.

The risk assessment should identify the risks associated with the work and enable the demolition contractor to select appropriate demolition solutions that remove or reduce the risks before the work commences.

The demolition contractor should then select the most suitable methods of demolition, which include measures to adequately control any remaining risks.

### 3.4.4 Method statement

Method statements should address the particular needs of the site and detail the planned sequences and methods of demolition. The proposed working methods should be assessed to determine whether a number of method statements are required, particularly where the operations are phased.

Method statements should be prepared in such a way that they enable supervisors and managers to ensure that persons on site are made aware of how the work is to be carried out, including the sequence of operations, the types of plant and equipment to be used and the precautions to be taken, as appropriate.

**Methods such as toolbox talks are recommended to help in disseminating the information, especially for those carrying out the work.**

Method statements should be regarded as live documents and modified as required to cater for planned changes in systems of work.

### 3.4.5 Health and safety file

The health and safety file is a record of information for the client or user of the premises. Its purpose is to inform anyone who might be responsible for the structure or site in the future, of the risks that will have to be managed during any maintenance, repair or renovation. Generally, for demolition work, the health and safety file will contain information such as details of the following.

- ☑ Any services that have been capped or discovered and worked around.
- ☑ The presence of any voids and details of any areas that may have been filled.
- ☑ The actions taken to remove or treat contaminated land.
- ☑ Asbestos removal from retained structures, including copies of the four-stage clearance certificate and disposal records.

Such information may be useful to add to the asbestos management plan for a site, or to provide confirmation for future use that contaminants have been removed from the site. A health and safety file is only required for projects involving more than one contractor.

## 3.4.6 Summary of statutory notifications

### 3.4.6.1 The Building Act

Where the volume of demolition exceeds 1,750 cubic feet, six weeks' advance notice must be given to the Local Authority Building Control Office, requesting permission for demolition.

### 3.4.6.2 CDM

Notifiable projects are initially notified to the enforcing authority on Form F10 by the client and may involve an additional notification if, for example, duty holders or the length of the contract changes.

### 3.4.6.3 Asbestos Regulations

14 days' notice on form ASB 5 must be given to the HSE, Office of Rail Regulation or Local Authority where work with licensable asbestos is involved.

### 3.4.6.4 Hazardous waste

Regulations require any site generating more than 500 kg of hazardous waste per year (for example, asbestos) to register with the Environment Agency (EA) for England, Natural Resources Wales (NRW) for Wales or the Scottish Environment Protection Agency (SEPA) for Scotland. (This can be completed online.) Advance applications must be made to the EA, NRW or SEPA to carry out a notifiable exempt waste management activity.

www.

**To register or renew as a hazardous waste producer refer to the Environment Agency website.**

## 3.5 Selection and appointment of a demolition contractor

The client or principal contractor, in selecting a demolition contractor, should satisfy themselves of the contractor's competence, knowledge, ability and resources to carry out the work safely.

Expertise is vital. If there is more than one contractor on site, the client has to appoint a competent principal designer and principal contractor to co-ordinate and manage the health and safety issues during the demolition works. The principal contractor's role may well be taken by the demolition contractor. References must be sought, and pertinent questions asked, to establish the credibility of the contractor involved. If there is only one contractor on site, there is no requirement to appoint a principal contractor or principal designer. The contractor and designer respectively will have to fulfil their duties in accordance with the CDM Regulations.

Care must be taken to ensure that the principal designer has the necessary level of competence in demolition work as it is a very specialist field. Alternatively, it may be prudent to consider appointing an independent demolition engineer as an adviser.

www.

**A useful source of information is the Institute of Demolition Engineers.**

## 3.5.1 Pre-qualification

If more than five people are employed by the demolition contractor, then that contractor should have a written health and safety policy, which should be divided into three separate parts.

- ☑ **Part 1.** A general statement of health and safety policy.
- ☑ **Part 2.** The organisation and structure of that policy with details of people who have responsibilities under this document.
- ☑ **Part 3.** Details of the practical arrangements for health and safety.

The health and safety policy should be signed and dated by the director responsible and communicated to employees.

The client should also consider the following.

- ☑ Does the contractor employ a health and safety adviser, or do they utilise the services of a health and safety adviser or consultants?
- ☑ Does the contractor employ a demolition engineer, or do they utilise the services of demolition consultants?
- ☑ If consultants are used, how often will they visit the site?
- ☑ If a competent demolition engineer is employed, what is their experience and competence?

  ***Note:*** *membership or fellowship of the Institute of Demolition Engineers (MIDE/FIDE) and/or the Construction Skills Certification scheme (CSCS) Professional qualified person (PQP) in Demolition, are a good indicator of competence.*
- ☑ Are the consultants experienced in the health and safety management requirements of demolition sites?
- ☑ Are the consultants always available for advice, particularly if something goes wrong?

F
03

The safety record of the contractor should also be considered.

- ☑ Are safety statistics for injuries, lost time and dangerous occurrences kept and available?
- ☑ Has the HSE issued any improvement or prohibition notices against the contractor? If so, have the root causes of such been resolved?
- ☑ Are there any pending potential enforcement actions against the contractor?
- ☑ Is it the intention to use sub-contractors? If so, for what elements and how do they select and control sub-contractors?
- ☑ Is the contractor a member of the NFDC?

Membership of this organisation is a useful Stage 1 (knowledge) competence indicator under CDM and will give the client the assurance of a minimum of five years' satisfactory trading experience, and a knowledge that certain recognised minimum standards have been and are being met (for example, insurance, training and supervision).

However, irrespective of membership of the NFDC, checks must be made regarding whether the organisation has the relevant experience (Stage 2) competence under CDM.

- ☑ Does the contractor have adequate public and employer's liability insurance that covers demolition?

Check for any restrictive covenants or other restrictions (for example, for work to be carried out above a height of 30 metres).

- ☑ Are the company's employees on the scheme for the certification of competence for demolition operatives (Levels 1, 2 or 3)?
- ☑ Are references available? It is useful to speak to a client from a similar job as well as from their last project.

### 3.5.2 Appointing a contractor

A genuine and competent demolition contractor will not object to supplying the name of the client for whom the last contract was carried out. If that client is then contacted, they can be asked whether they were satisfied with the work.

They can be asked for information on the works, type, size, approximate value and so on, and asked the following questions.

- ☑ Were any problems experienced during the works?
- ☑ How did the contractor perform overall?
- ☑ Would they use the contractor again?

These are just examples of the kinds of question that should be asked to ensure satisfaction when considering the appointment of such a contractor.

An interview with the potential contractor should be held to clarify matters. The client can also see if they would be prepared, or if they are qualified and competent, to take on the role of principal contractor.

## 3.6 Planning for demolition

**It cannot be emphasised too strongly that demolition is potentially hazardous and must be left to the experts (that is, competent persons). Experience, knowledge, training, planning and supervision are of paramount importance.**

Before any work starts, the implications of the demolition project to be carried out must be determined.

- ☑ What is the age of the building(s) and what was (were) the previous use(s)?
- ☑ What is the type of construction and what were the materials used?
- ☑ What is the scope and extent of the works?
- ☑ Is it full or partial demolition?
- ☑ Are floor slabs, foundations or piles to be removed?
- ☑ Where are the separation points, if any, and what are the perceived load paths?
- ☑ Are there any hazardous substances in, around or under the building, which are to be demolished (for example, asbestos, lead paints, flammable liquids, unidentified drums or packages, Japanese knotweed and so on)?
- ☑ Is asbestos suspected? If so, a full invasive refurbishment/demolition survey must be carried out to form part of the pre-construction information.
- ☑ Is the building on contaminated land?
- ☑ Are there any proximity hazards present (such as overhead or underground services, voids, tunnels and so on)?
- ☑ Are there any site restrictions (such as access and egress)?
- ☑ Are there people and adjacent properties that may be affected by the proposed working hours?
- ☑ Will people be affected by noise or vibration emanating from the site? If so, a Section 61 noise notice may be required.
- ☑ Will there be a need to carry out a dilapidation survey of the adjacent buildings and/or highways?

- ☑ Will any waste management licences or permits be required to process or reuse the demolished material?
- ☑ Is the project likely to be notifiable?
- ☑ Who will notify the Local Authority under the Building Act, Section 80 (>1,750 ft³)?

The information above would form the basis of the pre-construction information collected by the client, and assisted by the principal designer, under CDM.

Once these things have been determined, decisions should be taken as to what are the acceptable or unacceptable methods to carry out the demolition.

Information on contaminated land must include details of the past and current uses of the site. Advice can be sought from the EA, NRW or SEPA, and the Local Authority Environmental Health Department. This may result in a requirement for a site survey, including the taking, observation and analysis of core samples.

Two important final questions remain.

- ☑ How should the job and site be left safe?
- ☑ What is the timescale for the job to be carried out and is it sufficient for the demolition to be carried out safely?

The latter point is particularly relevant as CDM places a duty on the client to indicate the minimum project mobilisation period, with notifiable projects recording this period on the HSE notification form, F10.



## 3.7 Essential elements of a demolition health and safety plan

Some or all of the following points may be covered in the risk assessment and method statement for the proposed work.

### 3.7.1 Project information

Names, addresses, contacts and telephone numbers should be detailed indicating the client, project managers, quantity surveyors, architects, structural engineers, the principal designer and principal contractor.

### 3.7.2 Scope of work

An explicit and concise opening paragraph should be included, outlining the extent of work, along with any other related work (such as asbestos removal), items or equipment to be recovered and set aside, façade retention, and so on.

### 3.7.3 Existing environmental information and drawings

Where available, construction drawings should have been supplied to the contractor, by the client, along with information on the former use of the site or buildings to be demolished. This information should include the health and safety file for the premises (if available), to determine what (if any) physical or chemical hazards are on the site or in the buildings (such as underground tanks and/or potential chemical or biological hazards or contaminated land).

The details of the building or structure should be checked to ensure that it is not a listed building. In addition, the locality of the site in relation to schools, roads, hospitals and so on, which may be affected by the demolition activity, should be taken into account.

### 3.7.4 Risk assessment and special hazards

Having gathered all available information and visited the site to assess the work involved, along with identifying all known hazards and confined spaces, the contractor's appointed person on site should ensure that risk assessments, and assessments for asbestos, lead, Control of Substances Hazardous to Health (COSHH) or noise are made. Method statements should then be drawn up.

Information from these assessments should be included in the health and safety plan for the project, which must also take into consideration risks to health, and detail any safety precautions that are being taken to control and manage the risks.

Consideration must be given at an early stage to control the access for workers and any visitors and, where practicable, ensure separate access and egress for vehicles, plant and machinery.

Finally, assess the impact that the site environment will have on any people who might be affected by the activity (such as neighbours or members of the public).

**For further information on method statements and risk assessments, including examples of both, refer to Chapter A05 Risk assessments and method statements.**

### 3.7.5 Personnel and the appointed person

All persons on site are responsible for health and safety. The following have specific responsibility for health and safety and for supervision of the site.

- ☑ All designers.
- ☑ The principal contractor.
- ☑ The demolition contractor and specialist sub-contractors (for example, asbestos removal contractors).

- ☑ The director responsible for safety.
- ☑ The site safety adviser.
- ☑ The contracts manager.
- ☑ The appointed person – a competent demolition foreman.
- ☑ The person who has first aid or emergency aid training.
- ☑ All other contractors on site.

A method of recording who is on site must be rigorously maintained throughout the contract by signing in and out in the (daily) site register.

The principal contractor or contractor, with support from the appointed person and others, must ensure that the relevant sections of the health and safety plan are communicated to all people on site at appropriate intervals (such as site induction, task talks and toolbox talks).



These occasions should be recorded and signed for in order to indicate ownership by the recipients.

www.

**A card scheme for the certification of competence of demolition operatives is operated by CITB on behalf of the National Demolition Training Group.**

| | |
|---|---|
| **Green card** | Demolition trainee (temporary card) D0 (may indicate little or no experience). |
| **Red card** | Demolition, reclamation and refurbishment operative D1 (one year's experience or more). |
| **Blue card** | Demolition experienced worker (topman) D2a (two years' experience, depending on category). |
| **Blue card** | Demolition topman D2b (holds an experienced worker card and has achieved all appropriate units of NVQ/SVQ Level 2). |
| **Gold card** | Demolition supervisor experienced worker D3a (has passed the 12-week supervisors' course). |
| **Gold card** | Demolition supervisor D3b (holds an experienced worker card and has achieved the NVQ/SVQ Level 3). |
| **Black card** | Demolition manager D6a (has achieved the demolition manager five day course and assessment). |
| **Black card** | Demolition manager D6b (has achieved the NVQ/SVQ diploma Level 6). |

## 3.7.6 Programme

The programme time allocated must be adequate to allow the demolition work to be planned and carried out safely. This should detail the mobilisation and planning, and correct sequence of the works with any hold and review points.

Where the programme has unavoidable interfaces with other trades or contractors on site, this must be recognised as a potential area of risk. Good communications, planning and management are therefore essential to ensure high standards in health and safety.

The operator of crushing equipment must also give notice to their relevant Local Authority of their intention to carry out crushing work each time the equipment is moved.

## 3.7.7 Services

Before any work starts, all utility companies must be contacted by the client or, if agreed, by the principal contractor, and sent a site plan showing the footprint and extent of the planned demolition, with the proposed commencement date, requesting the disconnection or isolation of the appropriate service (in other words electricity, gas, water, telecommunications or other cables).

These requests should be made in good time and be acknowledged in writing by the relevant utility, with confirmation that the services have or will be isolated or disconnected.

Prior to their arrival on site, utility companies should be sent any relevant sections of the pre-construction information to incorporate within their own safe systems of work (for example, details of ground contamination and/or unsafe conditions or structures prevailing on site).

Where such disconnection is not possible, any pipes or cables should be clearly identified, marked and protected to ensure that they are not disturbed during the works.

Disconnection confirmation in writing must be received and be on site before any demolition work commences.

Finally, if in doubt over any services, the contractor should seek further advice from the utility provider, specialist services contractor or services consultants.

If overhead power lines are present, care needs to be taken, particularly where machines, cranes, excavators or demolition machines with high reach are to be operated. Adequate control measures should be put in place (such as warning goalposts) following advice from the relevant power supply company or National Grid.

**For further information refer to Chapter D08 Underground and overhead services.**

## 3.7.8 Lead

Exposure risks from lead paint, dust and fumes are most likely to occur in pre-1970 buildings, especially during repair, maintenance, refurbishment and demolition, if proper precautions are not followed. It should be noted that, wherever paintwork/coatings are likely to be damaged or disturbed, the HSE advises lead (paint) surveys **regardless of the age of the building or the extent of the works.**

**Information on reducing the health risks in construction work can be found on the HSE website.**

**For further information refer to Chapter B12 Lead.**



## 3.7.9 Asbestos

Under Asbestos Regulations, there is a duty on building owners and/or the tenants 'duty holder(s)' to identify (via asbestos surveys) and manage the presence of asbestos in the non-domestic properties under their control. HSE publication HSG264 provides the following guidance.

- ☑ The types of survey.
- ☑ The circumstances in which either type of survey would be required.
- ☑ Appointing a competent asbestos surveyor.
- ☑ The exchange of information that is necessary between all interested parties.
- ☑ Avoiding caveats whereby some areas would not be surveyed.
- ☑ What should be expected by way of a survey report.

The regulations state that all asbestos-containing materials should be removed prior to demolition, so far as is reasonably practicable. They also require that the necessary planning actions and notifications are carried out.

The management process should be based on the information gained from a refurbishment/demolition asbestos survey, carried out before contractors are invited to tender for the demolition. This should include a drawing of the building footprint (all floors) and a list of the approximate amounts and locations of asbestos-containing materials found. Simply writing 'throughout the building' is not acceptable and the client should be informed that the survey is inadequate. The survey should be checked for any exclusions (caveats) or areas not accessed and for any specific recommendations. However, it should be noted that such clauses are generally unacceptable, as detailed in HSG264.

If the survey identifies licensable asbestos materials (typically asbestos insulation, coatings and insulating board), which require a licensed contractor, then 14 days must be allowed for the notification process to the enforcing authority, usually the HSE.

All non-licensed work (for example, removal of asbestos cement sheets) needs to be carried out with the appropriate controls in place. However, for notifiable non-licensed work (NNLW) additional requirements have to be met, including notifying the relevant authority of the work with asbestos, ensuring medical examinations are carried out and maintaining registers of work. Some examples of NNLW are removal involving textured coatings, where the method of removal requires deterioration of the material, and removal of asbestos paper and cardboard products, if not firmly bonded in products.

**Notification of notifiable non-licensed work can be made online using form ASB NNLW1.**

**It is the responsibility of the person in charge of the job to assess the asbestos-containing material to be worked on and decide whether the work is non-licensed work or NNLW.**

From the survey, an inventory of asbestos-containing materials should be made and ticked off as they are removed. This should prevent creating risk during soft strip and demolition.

There are many occasions when asbestos-containing materials are only revealed during the demolition.

All operatives and machine drivers must receive regular training in basic asbestos recognition (minimum half-day asbestos awareness course) so that they can recognise materials that could be, or contain, asbestos and stop work and take appropriate advice. Annual refresher training is mandatory for all workers who handle or come into contact with asbestos-containing materials.

**For advice on suitable awareness training refer to the HSE website.**

**Asbestos guidance note *Industry guidance for non-licensed work with asbestos-containing materials within a demolition or refurbishment environment* is available from the NFDC.**

## 3.8 Methods of demolition

This section gives an outline of the types of demolition techniques commonly employed with a view to giving the reader an appreciation of the demolition activity.

The key to a successful demolition project is to ensure that the appropriate risk assessments and method statements have been developed to identify the correct sequence of carrying out the work, together with the necessary tools, equipment and people required. These must be recorded in writing, fit for purpose, clearly communicated and understood by the persons using them.

### 3.8.1 Partial demolition

Partial demolition is often carried out where refurbishment is being undertaken and can include façade retention. In any demolition, daily or, if required, more frequent checks should be carried out to confirm the stability of the remaining structure.

If at any time during the demolition the structure appears or becomes unsafe, all workers should be withdrawn until actions have been taken to remove any danger.

This may involve the use of mini machines (such as skid steers and/or mini excavators). Therefore, an assessment of the floor-loading capacity should be undertaken by a competent person (such as a structural engineer) to take into account the dead and live loads, any necessity for temporary works (such as propping, shoring and so on).

### 3.8.2 Progressive (top-down) demolition

Progressive demolition is generally carried out in the reverse order to construction, and often follows the soft strip-out phase.

This is the most commonly used method of demolishing structures and should be detailed in the health and safety plan.

In high-rise buildings where a floor-by-floor demolition is being carried out, danger points, such as the following, should be recognised.

- Structural stability.
- On-floor loadings (machinery and arisings).
- Falling debris.
- Slips, trips and falls.
- Maintaining clear access and egress.
- Risk of fire hazards.
- The need for secure edge protection.

**The NFDC has produced guidance on demolishing multistorey structures of 18 m and above, and in the use of high and ultra high-reach demolition machines to improve user and procurer awareness.**

### 3.8.3 Demolition by designed collapse mechanism

Demolition by designed collapse can be achieved by pre-weakening the structure, followed by explosive displacement of important structural elements, remote mechanical demolition by a demolition machine, high-reach demolition rig or crawler crane or similar, or occasionally by pulling it down, using a wire rope.

When explosives are being considered, only fully qualified explosive engineers should be used (for example, members of the Institute of Explosives Engineers).

### 3.8.4 Manual demolition techniques

Manual demolition techniques are used when other methods of demolition are not suitable or possible (for example, city centre or confined sites, where there is insufficient space around the structure for remote mechanical demolition).

Some of the types of tools or operations that can be used in manual demolition are listed below.

- Hand tools.
- Breakers, compressors or hammers.
- Concrete nibblers or hydraulic pulverisers.
- Stitch drilling.
- Drilling and hydraulic bursting.
- Drilling and expansive pastes.
- Oxy-propane cutting equipment.
- Diamond cutting and sawing.

For brick or concrete structures:

- identify any pre-stressed or post-tensioned concrete beams, columns and trusses that may be present within the structure and determine a safe method of demolition
- wherever practicable, carry out demolition in the reverse order to construction
- maintain tools in good condition, and use them safely
- use compressed air or portable electric power tools, from a 110 volt supply
- make operatives fully aware of the safe procedures
- recognise the potential exposure to high levels of noise and vibration requiring assessments and the associated control measures
- in addition to site induction, ensure task and toolbox talks are prepared, delivered and understood at key stages of the work.

As far as is reasonably practicable, employees should not work above each other and care must be taken to ensure that debris does not drop into working or otherwise occupied areas.

If lift or service shafts or other openings through floors are used to drop debris down, the lift car, services and equipment must be cleared in advance to remove any snagging points, openings must be adequately protected by either suitable guard-rails and toe-boards (with no gap between guard-rails and toe-boards exceeding 470 mm) or by other substantial, effective barriers. It may not be possible to guard an opening where plant (such as a skid steer) is being used to bulldoze arisings into a shaft or chute. In such cases a safe system of work must be developed, which is sufficiently robust to:

- stop the item of plant falling into the chute or shaft
- control when materials will be loaded and unloaded to stop materials being tipped onto someone below
- protect other workers from falling down the shaft.

It is still acceptable to use window openings as a means of removing debris from upper floors under certain conditions. The opening would have to be protected to prevent operatives falling whilst throwing the debris out. Furthermore, the landing zone (that is, the elevation to receive the materials arising from the soft stripping or demolition operations) must be clearly identified and completely protected so that materials cannot fall on anyone. Typically the area (drop zone) will be fenced off with mobile fence panels and then the material loaded with an excavator into a hook bin container; this area should be controlled by a banksperson to ensure that no entry can be effected by unauthorised persons.

If the structure has more than two storeys, consideration should be given to the prevailing wind conditions as well as creating an enclosed scaffold chute.

With regard to falling materials and exposed edges, where necessary, hazard areas (personnel exclusion zones) must be created in accordance with the requirements of current regulations and good practice.

### 3.8.4.1 Provision and use of work equipment

The Provision and Use of Work Equipment Regulations (PUWER) covers equipment used in demolition. They require that an employer supplies work equipment that is safe, correct and suitable for the job, and that the equipment is maintained.

Demolition can involve some work being carried out at height, particularly salvage and soft stripping (for example, the recovery of slates), which has in the past been the cause of deaths and injuries to demolition operatives. Due to advances in demolition techniques, and the increasing size and reach of the machines used, there is now a reduced need to work at height. However, the presence of such machines on site brings about responsibilities for servicing, maintenance, thorough inspections, operator competence and so on under these regulations.

Under the regulations, falling object protection is required for machinery. A demolition specification machine must have a cab guard, as it is foreseeable when working overhead that material could fall onto the cab. Demolition attachments are common on a demolition site. Quick hitch couplers requiring the fitting of a safety pin when changing attachments should never be operated without that pin being in place. The use of reinforcing bars as makeshift retaining pins for attachments would be contrary to these regulations.

It is common to see mobile crushers employed during a demolition project to process the demolition arisings for reuse as part of ongoing works on site. These machines can pose a great risk to untrained or unaware operatives on site. Issues such as machinery guarding and clearing blockages, as well as dust, noise and vibration, must be considered.

Safe working practices dictate that operators should avoid standing on a crusher whilst it is running (for example, trying to remove foreign objects from the demolition arisings) or near the crushing jaws.

www. **For further information refer to the NFDC guidance on demolition attachments.**

### 3.8.4.2 Oxy-propane cutting equipment

The use of oxy-propane cutting equipment requires the following.

- Operatives are trained and competent in the safe use of the equipment.
- Appropriate PPE is used (such as the correct mask, goggles and hand or arm protection).
- The equipment is inspected and tested for leaks before use.

- ☑ Cylinders are secured in an upright position.
- ☑ Hoses are secured with crimped fittings, not jubilee clips.
- ☑ Flashback arresters are always fitted between cylinder gauges and hoses.
- ☑ Spare cylinder storage areas are separated by a gap of at least three metres between oxygen and propane bottles.

Do not:

- ☒ operate hot cutting equipment within an enclosed space because of fumes, leakage of fuel and/or oxygen gases
- ☒ use oxygen to blow dust off clothing
- ☒ carry or use petrol or gas lighters to ignite the cutting torch (use only approved flint guns)
- ☒ rely on existing site fire points (ensure additional fire extinguishers are in place prior to commencement of hot works).

Whenever oxy-propane cutting equipment is used, the correct fire-fighting equipment must always be available. All operatives should be trained in the safe use of fire extinguishers.

Hot work should generally be stopped for an agreed period before leaving site, typically one hour before finishing, to avoid the potential of fire.

**For more information refer to Chapter C02 Fire prevention and control.**

## 3.8.5 Mechanical demolition techniques

Machinery should be fit for purpose, used in safe working spaces, adequately protected (for example, by roll-over protective structures (ROPS) and/or falling object protective structures (FOPS)) and operated by authorised, competent persons (for example, holding a CPCS card for the appropriate category of machine).

### 3.8.5.1 Remote control demolition

Remote demolition is generally carried out by specialised equipment, often in hazardous or aggressive environments (for example, nuclear installations). The use of pedestrian operated machines is becoming more common and they offer possible solutions to the difficulties of complying with the problems of noise and vibration experienced during hand demolition.

These types of machine are particularly useful where the machine is breaking out the structure of the floor above, and/or when the operating surface is being progressively removed as the operator can stand well clear of the danger area.

### 3.8.5.2 Using a 360° adapted demolition rig with multi-functional attachments

This type of demolition machine is commonly used to demolish relatively low level buildings, or is used after other height reduction techniques have been carried out.

The machine should always be positioned at a safe distance from the structure, taking into account the height of the structure and the build up of debris as it is reduced. In situations where the machine operator cannot see all elevations of the structure or in circumstances where external influences may dictate stopping the work until such distractions have been annulled, a bankssperson or lookout may be required to assist the operator. The bankssperson or lookout should be positioned in a safe location, outside of the machine's operational, personnel exclusion zone and predicted debris zone, and preferably within sight of the operator (or in radio contact, where this is not possible).

Whilst the machine driver is isolated from noise and dust, the bankssperson or lookout is not, and may need to wear additional PPE depending on the findings of the risk assessments for the work being done (for example, impact-resistant goggles if an impact hammer is being used).

The height of the wall or building to be demolished should not normally be greater than the maximum reach of the machine; this maintains a safe distance between the machine and the structure being demolished.

In some circumstances, it is appropriate and practicable to create a ramp for the machine to sit on to increase the reach using rubble from previous demolition. Care must be taken to ensure the ramp and operating platform are properly designed and constructed and that there has been sufficient compaction to avoid the machine sitting on an unstable base.

It is not recommended to construct a ramp within a building, due to potentially overloading the floors or surcharging the outside walls.

It is not recommended to allow undermining or undercutting of structures when the machine cannot reach the top of the building. Any contractor suggesting this method should consider selecting a larger (higher reach) machine to avoid putting the operator at unnecessary risk from falling structures and debris.

### 3.8.5.3 Super high-reach 360° excavators

Typically these machines have a reach of between 15 and 65+ m, plus the length of the fitted attachments for shearing concrete or steel structural elements. To ensure a safe distance between the machine and the structure, a ratio of 2:1 height to distance must be maintained for machines up to 45 m reach. In some cases this may mean that the recommended maximum working height for the machine is restricted to 75% of its maximum reach.

A useful visual indicator that the machine is working within safe limits is when the dipper (the last section of the excavator's arm) is horizontal or approximately 90° to the boom.

These sophisticated machines are fitted with variable width tracks and are heavier than standard machines, thus giving increased ground-bearing pressure and extended working envelopes. It is vital that ground conditions are known and any voids and ducts, located where the machine will track, are identified, clearly marked (fenced off) and, where possible, adequately filled and compacted. In terms of ground conditions, these machines should be considered more as a crane or piling frame in terms of stability, rather than an excavator.

Operator training is supported by a specialist CPCS category for high-reach machines with various endorsements for different reach machines (for example, up to 15 m, 30 m and 30 m+).

It is essential for operators to understand how to operate the machines safely and also have knowledge of good practice with regard to fitting and changing attachments. The manufacturer or the supplier of the machinery can provide advice on this. There are further CPCS card endorsements for this activity.

www.

**A publication called *High-reach demolition rigs – Guidance notes* is available to members from the National Federation of Demolition Contractors.**

### 3.8.5.4 Hydraulic pusher arm

Demolition using a hydraulic pusher arm is occasionally used for removing masonry structures. However, with the advent of super high-reach machines with multi-functional attachments, it is almost obsolete now and its use should only be carried out by experts. It is therefore not covered within the scope of this chapter.

Before using the demolition equipment, steps must be taken to ensure that the building is completely empty and that all services are isolated with the appropriate written disconnection confirmation on site.

Because of the danger of debris falling onto the demolition rig and its driver, the machine should be a safe distance from the structure and be fitted with a cab guard and, as an added precaution, it should be fitted with shatterproof glass.

### 3.8.5.5 Demolition ball

Demolition using a ball is extremely rare due to the advent of super high-reach machines. When a ball is used, the crane equipment must be heavy duty and only drop or pendulum (for example, in line with the jib) balling techniques should be employed.

When a ball is employed, regular (for example, hourly) inspections of the equipment must take place, paying particular attention to the attachments and shackles.

Arrangements for safely rectifying the situation should be in place in the event of the demolition ball becoming trapped within the structure.

Further detail is not appropriate within the scope of this chapter.

## 3.8.6 Bridges or steel structure demolition

The demolition of bridges, pylons, masts, or similar, requires specialised planning and techniques. The information provided below can be used as a guide, but specific detail is not covered within the scope of this chapter.

An assessment by a demolition engineer and/or a structural engineer should be undertaken.

A comprehensive safe working plan must be developed providing a safety assessed means of access, using a competent crane hire company and experienced slingers and signallers to ensure compliance with the Lifting Operations and Lifting Equipment Regulations.

For bridges that run over roads, or cross railway lines, liaison must take place with the Highways Department of the Local Authority involved or Network Rail, as appropriate.

**For further information refer to Chapter C07 Lifting operations.**

## 3.9 Environmental and other considerations

Noise, dust, fumes, vibration and fire controls need to be properly addressed before and during the demolition operation. Consideration should be given to the following points.

### 3.9.1 Noise

Where demolition operations are carried out in locations likely to affect the general public, the Local Authority may request the principal contractor to submit an application under Section 61 of the Control of Pollution Act (COPA), specifying working methods, working hours and maximum noise levels (called prior consent). A Local Authority can issue an abatement notice (Section 60 notice) for failure to comply with Section 61 consent conditions, or where noise levels are creating a statutory nuisance.

In accordance with regulations, where noise levels are above (or expected to be above) the lower exposure action value, the demolition contractor must ensure that a noise assessment has been carried out and that, where possible, people are kept out of the danger area.

Any machinery that is to be used in the demolition process should, as far as possible, be fitted and used with soundproofing or noise reducing equipment (such as exhaust silencers).

Where it is necessary for people to work within the area of noisy operations, adequate hearing protection must be provided and used as necessary. If the upper exposure action value, 85 dB(A), is exceeded, or likely to be exceeded, hearing protection must be worn and hearing protection zones clearly indicated.

Where the findings of a risk assessment indicate that the hearing of any employee is at risk due to noise exposure at work, health surveillance, including hearing checks, must be provided.

**BS 5228 gives advice on the provisions for noise control on demolition sites. For further guidance refer to Chapter E06 Statutory nuisance.**

### 3.9.2 Dust

Nearly all demolition work creates dust and many require a COSHH assessment (for example, respirable crystalline silica).

Taking simple precautions (such as the following) ensures the dust nuisance can be reduced to a minimum.

- Implementing techniques that reduce dust generation.
- The use of light water sprays both before and during demolition are very effective. However, consideration should be given to any potential run-off contaminants that may be produced and to the proximity of demolition work to electrical services, retained structures and drains.
- Where demolition is being carried out inside a building and water sprays are inappropriate, local ventilation, using air movers and filters, can help to alleviate dust levels. (It may also be possible to create voids in the structure by taking out, for instance, walls and partitions.)
- Dust masks, as any other PPE, should be used only as a last resort. Where any mask is used, the wearer must be face-fit tested for the mask.
- Consideration should be given to ascertaining the type of dust the operative is exposed to and measuring the actual dust levels to confirm whether or not the anticipated levels are being achieved and thereby whether the measures being taken (for example, personal and perimeter pumps) are effective.

**For further guidance refer to Chapter B10 Dust and fumes.**

### 3.9.3 Asbestos

Asbestos was widely used in the UK until it was banned in late 1999; disturbance of the fabric of any building built before this time has the potential to expose asbestos.

As previously referred to under 'Planning for demolition', where there is a remote risk of asbestos containing materials being present, a comprehensive invasive asbestos survey, in accordance with HSG264, must be undertaken prior to contractors being invited to tender for the demolition.

Where asbestos is present, the necessary planning, actions and notifications must be implemented to comply with the Control of Asbestos Regulations. The principles of these regulations are to prevent the exposure to and spread of asbestos by training and adequate control measures.

**For further information and guidance refer to Chapter B09 Asbestos.**

### 3.9.4 Fumes

A cutting torch, used on steelwork, may produce toxic gases (such as nitrogen dioxide). If a phosphate coating is present, phosphine may be produced. If a chlorinated solvent has been used, sulphides may be formed, which have no smell until high toxic levels are present. Toxic metal fumes may additionally be given off.

Attention is drawn particularly to lead (lead-painted steelwork), cadmium (cadmium bolt heads) and zinc.

Before any hot work cutting is allowed, available information or paint samples may be required for analysis, a COSHH assessment should be undertaken, and the necessary control measures implemented.

Operatives undertaking hot work must be issued with the appropriate PPE, including respiratory protective equipment (RPE), as necessary.

**For further information refer to:**

- ☑ **Chapter B07 Control of substances hazardous to health**
- ☑ **Chapter B10 Dust and fumes**
- ☑ **Chapter B12 Lead.**



### 3.9.5 Vibration

Vibration from demolition operations can cause damage to adjacent property and injury to personnel working on site or, in extreme cases, to members of the public. Exposure to vibration must be controlled in accordance with the requirements of the Control of Vibration at Work Regulations.

- ☑ Where possible avoid the need to expose persons and/or property to vibration by selecting appropriate demolition techniques.
- ☑ Attempts should be made to establish the presence of any existing sources of vibration and whether vibration monitors are needed in sensitive locations.
- ☑ Where buildings adjoining those to be demolished are being retained, separation should be carried out using hand tools rather than machinery.
- ☑ Necessary precautions should be taken or alternative equipment considered to alleviate the risk of permanent physical injury caused by hand-arm vibration syndrome (HAVS) (for example, vibration white finger, from continued use of vibrating tools).

With regard to the last point, the exposure time for most demolition hand tools is extremely short, and the contractor will need a robust policy that includes health surveillance to carry out hand demolition using pneumatic electric or hydraulic demolition picks.

**For further information refer to Chapter B14 Vibration and to the *Code of Practice for noise and vibration control on construction and open sites* (BS 5228).**

### 3.9.6 Fire and explosion risks

Where flammable liquids, gases or vapours have been used, or released in a building that is under demolition, any equipment, tank or pipes, which could have contained such substances, must be purged and tested for explosive gases prior to work taking place. Any such work should be done under a permit to work system.

General hot work, using oxygen and propane cutting equipment, should be carried out only by operatives trained in its safe and proper use, wearing the appropriate PPE, including goggles, gloves, overalls and respiratory protection equipment.

If the occasional burning of debris (such as wood or paper) is allowed on site, the fire must be as small as possible, well away from buildings, roadways and fuel stores, and kept under constant supervision.

Before any burning of debris is undertaken, consideration needs to be given to waste management licensing, or any local by-laws, which may prohibit such actions taking place. Penalties for the contravention of such conditions can be severe in some circumstances.

All fires must be completely extinguished at least one hour before work stops for the day and checked again, to ensure there are no glowing embers, before operatives leave the site.

Adequate fire-fighting equipment must be available, with fire points containing extinguishers in prominent and well-marked areas adjacent to the demolition hot work operations.

**For further information refer to Chapter C02 Fire prevention and control.**

## 3.9.7 Recycling

Demolition works should always take into account the propensity for reuse, reclamation and/or recylcing of materials. A material survey of the site will identify what materials are on site and how they may be recovered, managed and removed to maximise recovery. Where relevant, the contractor can opt to use a site waste management plan to record such material.

**For further details refer to Chapter E03 Waste management.**



In addition to removing recoverable items from demolition operations, it is common to crush the resultant brick and concrete into a sub-base material for future construction purposes.

- ☑ Crushing on site will generally take place when environmental conditions permit such actions. Environmental emissions (noise, fumes and dust) are considered as statutory nuisances and should therefore be eliminated or reduced to the lowest possible level. Regular monitoring of all control measures are required daily and should be recorded on a check sheet. Operations should cease if there are excessive emissions, which detrimentally affect conditions and people outside of the site boundary.
- ☑ Crushers must be registered with the supplier's own Local Authority, which must be notified in advance each time the equipment is moved.
- ☑ All materials to be recycled should be checked for any contaminants and dealt with in the correct manner to the required specification (for example, 6F2). The reuse of construction and demolition waste may require an environmental permit or relevant exemption. Advice should be sought from the local environment agency waste licensing officer on a case-by-case basis where any doubt may arise.
- ☑ Operatives working on the crushers and screeners must be properly trained (both general training on the use of crushers and screeners and specific training in respect of the equipment being used).
- ☑ Serious consideration must be given to the need for machinery guarding. A daily check sheet should be completed by the operator, which confirms that all guards are in place and the emergency stops are working.
- ☑ Robust safe systems of work are required to deal with blockages. These often happen because the operator loading the crusher or screener overfeeds the belt or because lumps are too big for the machine to process. The machine operator feeding the crusher or screener should sort the materials prior to loading by removing the timber, metals, plastics, fabrics, and so on that have entered the stockpile.
- ☑ All crusher and screener operators are required to wear suitable and adequate hearing protection and may require hearing checks and monitoring as the noise levels can be high.
- ☑ Dust suppression systems can be an effective, operational, engineering control, if fitted and working correctly. Half masks are preferred to the use of disposable paper masks as these will offer a higher level of protection. A risk assessment will be required to determine the appropriate type of RPE. Face-fit testing will be required following this.
- ☑ Operators should not be allowed to stand on an operating crusher, and must never stand near the jaws where the feedstock is being crushed. The risks arising from this practice can be combated at source by effective soft stripping and, if necessary, allowing picking from a product belt (in other words, before or after it has gone through the crusher).

## 3.9.8 Removal and disposal of materials

Before any materials are removed from site, both vehicular access to, and egress from, the site must be agreed with all concerned.

It is prudent, if practicable, to leave the floor slabs, roads and hard standings in place until the end of the project to avoid mud and other debris being carried out onto the highway. Where necessary, bog mats and wheel-washing facilities should be provided to ensure that debris is not carried onto the highway.

Depending on the nature of the material, covering lorries to stabilise the load and prevent dust and debris being released may be appropriate.

Daily records (duty of care note) must be kept of materials taken off site.

It is the responsibility of the demolition contractor to ensure that the carrier they are using is registered with the EA, NRW or SEPA, and that non-hazardous waste is accompanied with a duty of care controlled waste transfer document. These care documents must be kept for a minimum of two years by carriers and producers.

For hazardous waste (such as asbestos) the reception site must be registered with the relevant environment agency and a hazardous waste consignment note must accompany all such waste leaving site. These are available from the EA, NRW or SEPA on request, and you should retain the consignor's original (white copy). All such documentation should be kept for a minimum of three years.

**The demolition industry has developed demolition and refurbishment information data sheets (DRIDS) to help identify waste streams and explain how they can be reused or recycled. For an example refer to Appendix B.**

**For further information regarding DRIDs refer to the NFDC website.**

## 3.10 Monitoring the work

The key to a successful and safe demolition project is to plan, implement, monitor and maintain a safe system of work.

### Daily inspection by the site supervisor and/or client

- ☑ Provide daily briefings to the workforce on complex projects.
- ☑ Check for continuing safe working practices.
- ☑ Ensure access and egress routes are properly maintained.
- ☑ Ensure the site is kept tidy and, as far as possible, free from any piles of combustible rubbish.
- ☑ Ensure that sufficient signs are available and clearly visible to warn of hazardous areas and activities.
- ☑ Check the contractor's operatives are continuing to wear suitable protective equipment.
- ☑ Check the progress and sequence of the job to ensure that it complies with the health and safety plan.
- ☑ Check that an approved safe system of work is being followed.

## Appendix A – Definitions and terms used by the demolition industry

### General

| | |
|---|---|
| **CCDO** | Certificate of Competence for Demolition Operatives, affiliated to the CSCS scheme (Level 1, 2 and 3 operatives). |
| **Competent person in demolition** | Someone who has practical and theoretical knowledge, with actual experience, of the type of demolition that is taking place on the site. This person is generally accepted to be on site full time as the person responsible for the demolition activity. |
| **Demolition** | The deliberate pulling down, destruction or taking apart of a structure or a substantial part of a structure. It includes dismantling for re-erection or reuse. |
| **Exclusion zone** | An area where people are fully (sometimes partially) excluded during a demolition activity. This zone should be determined by a competent person, detailed in the health and safety plan, and may need to be defined by physical barriers on site. |
| **Explosives demolition** | This involves the designed collapse of a structure using controlled explosives. It is normally preceded by the removal of hazardous materials (for example, asbestos, soft stripping and pre-weakening of the structure). |
| **Façade retention** | Where the outer wall of a building or structure is retained in its original position during the demolition phase. It is usually supported by a façade retention system, internal or external. |
| **Fan** | A protective screen fixed to scaffolding to contain falling debris during demolition. Any fan must be designed to withstand the intended load. |
| **Felling** | The designed collapse of a structure in such a way that the debris falls in a predetermined area. |
| **Hot work** | The application of heat (including the use of tools that can produce an incendiary spark). It generally uses oxygen and propane gas cutting equipment. |
| **Party wall structures** | These are as defined under the Party Wall etc. Act and are typically where common structures (horizontal and vertical) exist between two or more parties. There are responsibilities to comply with when work affects a party wall structure. |
| **Propping and shoring** | A system of temporary supports to prevent movement. |
| **Remote mechanical demolition** | This normally involves the use of excavators, including high-reach machines fitted with attachments (see below) or, occasionally, a crawler crane with a demolition wrecking ball to create progressive controlled collapse of the structure. |
| **Safe working spaces** | Areas where demolition work is taking place, often protected by physical barriers (for example, machines protected by ROPs, FOPs and FOGs as applicable). |
| **Top-down demolition** | This generally involves demolition in a reverse sequence to its construction. |

### Machine-mounted attachments

| | |
|---|---|
| **Combination cutter** | A tool that can crush concrete and also cut steel reinforcing bar. |
| **Demolition ball** | A cast steel ball (drops or pendulum swings in line with the jib) used to demolish a structure. (Slew balling, although rarely used now, may be unacceptable as it places very high stresses on the crane.) |
| **Grapple** | A powered claw for handling waste and recycled material. |
| **Impact hammer** | A large breaker, mounted on an excavator, and usually powered by hydraulics (occasionally by compressed air). |
| **Pedestrian operated** | Pedestrian operated, boom equipped, tracked machine. |
| **Pulveriser** | Hydraulically powered jaws for crushing concrete. It may be hand/machine/crane mounted. |
| **Pusher arm** | An extension to an excavator, which enables it to carry out high-reach demolition. |
| **Quick hitch coupler** | A device fitted to the dipper arm of the excavator that allows a mechanical change of attachments quickly and efficiently. |
| **Rotator** | A part of an attachment fitted between the tool and the end of the dipper arm of the excavator, which allows the tool to be turned. Essential for most work in restricted sites. |
| **Shear** | Powered jaws for cutting metal or concrete. |

# Appendix B – Demolition and refurbishment information data sheets

National Federation of Demolition Contractors
**Voice of the Global Demolition Industry**

## DRIDS

Demolition Refurbishment Information Data Sheets

Enter your post code
Members Login

HOME | ABOUT US | DRIDS | CONTACT | NFDC

Search for DRIDS | GO

HOME / DRIDS / METAL / M1 STEEL

## M1 STEEL

M1

Steel Metal 17 04 05

Steel is an alloy of iron, carbon and other elements that are added for strength, lighter weight and corrosion resistance. Steel sections are produced in various styles, sizes and thicknesses, depending on the specification required. They are commonly rolled steel joists, I-beams, T-bars, H-sections, tubes, channels and mesh. They are of varying quality and finish to suit both structural and architectural finish.

## WASTE STREAMS

| INTRODUCTION | RECLAIM & REUSE | RECYCLE | RECOVERY | DISPOSAL |
|---|---|---|---|---|

The demolition industry is committed to ensuring that the most efficient and environmentally friendly waste stream is chosen for your demolition arisings. Please hover the disposal routes to view the waste options available for this material.

Register your facility today! | Suggest a material for inclusion

You must be logged in to use this system to create waste management plans - please contact the NFDC to create an account.

## USAGE & PROBABLE LOCATIONS

## PERSONAL PROTECTIVE EQUIPMENT

## REMOVAL, SEGREGATION & STORAGE

## TOOLS

## FIXTURES, FITTINGS & CONNECTIONS

*(Reproduced with permission from NFDC National Federation of Demolition Contractors.)*

F
03

F
03

# 04
# Shopfitting and interior contracting

**Contents**

## Overview

**The nature of shopfitting and interior contracting can give rise to additional challenges, including working in and around live retail environments, tight site logistics, out-of-hours working and congested sites.**

**This chapter highlights some of the main issues. However most topics encountered on site are common issues and are addressed in other sections of this publication.**



## 4.1 Introduction

Shopfitting refers to the sector of the construction industry requiring the manufacture and installation of bespoke furniture for interior environments. It should always be remembered that health and safety in all such projects begins the moment the enquiry lands on the estimator's desk.

The term **interior environment** incorporates retail (shops), non-retail (banks, building societies, museums and offices) and leisure (leisure centres, restaurants, pubs and garden centres). This is not exhaustive, but it does illustrate the examples of where this work is conducted.

Essentially anywhere there is an interior environment will be relevant to this chapter.

Shopfitting and interior contracting is fundamentally about developing and generating a strategy of **'Safe place – Safe person'.**

Managing those inherent risks in this sector is therefore the background to this approach.

### Safety failings

Following a recent case where a high street retailer was fined £1 million for safety failings and the contractor was also fined for failing to protect the general public, an HSE spokesperson said: 'this outcome should act as a wake-up call that any shopfitting refurbishment programmes involving asbestos-containing materials must be properly resourced, both in terms of time and money – no matter what. Large retailers and other organisations that carry out major refurbishment works must give contractors enough time and space within the store to carry out the works safely. Where this is not done, and construction workers and the public are put at risk, HSE will not hesitate in taking robust enforcement action'.

Refurbishing interior environments can and does bring a unique set of hazards, which clearly sets this sector apart from base build construction. These can then be sub-divided into the following categories.

- ☑ Sheds (out of town).
- ☑ High street.
- ☑ Shopping centres.
- ☑ Existing buildings.

## 4.2 Identifying risk

The nature of shopfitting and interior contracting can give rise to additional challenges (such as working in and around live retail environments, tight site logistics, out-of-hours working and congested sites).

From a health and safety focus **before the project commences** the fit-out team should give serious consideration to how they intend to manage the following.

- ☑ Difference between new build interior and revamp of an existing interior.
- ☑ Meccano job (removal of some fittings) or full refit (strip back to the original shell).
- ☑ Client-appointed contractors – managed by the principal contractor from the commencement of works.
- ☑ Third-party liability (general public/store staff).
- ☑ Merchandisers.
- ☑ Site logistics.
- ☑ Project team and retail team.
- ☑ Asbestos (a survey, where appropriate, should be provided before works commence).
- ☑ Fire safety.
- ☑ Possible vermin infestation.
- ☑ Carrying out the work whilst the premises continue to trade, if applicable.

### Fatal incident at a retail unit undergoing refurbishment

A recent fatal incident involving a shopfitting contractor has highlighted the need for clients, designers and contractors to be aware of the structural condition of existing works.

If in doubt a structural engineer should be seconded to the project to assist in managing the risk of accidental collapse.

**Everyone controlling site work has health and safety responsibilities.**

Checking that working conditions are healthy and safe before work begins, and ensuring that the proposed work is not going to put others at risk, requires planning and organisation.

This applies whatever the size of the site.



## 4.3 Site-based issues

Site-based issues that need to be considered during shopfitting contracts are listed below.

- ☑ **Site induction** – ensuring all workers attend a full, site-specific induction, especially during busy weekend and night time working shifts.
- ☑ **Hoardings** – phasing and safe erection.
- ☑ **Structural design** and temporary works following design.
- ☑ **Live services** – identification and isolation, installation of temporary electrics.
- ☑ **Occupational health** – noise, especially in internal spaces, and hand-arm vibration.
- ☑ **Dust** – breathing in construction dust is a high health risk and must be controlled.
- ☑ **Welfare** – provision of suitable welfare in restricted spaces to accommodate peak numbers of workers.
- ☑ **Waste management** – space constraints give rise to challenges of segregation and avoiding build up of wastes and providing chutes.
- ☑ **Fire** – maintaining integrity of existing fire arrangements, additional risks posed by construction work and avoiding build up of waste.
- ☑ **Working at height** – prevention of falls and selection and correct use of suitable access equipment.
- ☑ **Plant and equipment** – use of 110 volts, access for equipment, managing cartridge tools and gas nail guns and selection due to space constraints.
- ☑ **Logistics** – planning removal of waste and delivery and distribution of materials and large prefabricated items.
- ☑ **Manual handling** – planning is vital to ensure materials are distributed to minimise manual handling, utilising mechanical means and early or phased deliveries.
- ☑ **Personal protective equipment** and clothing – ensuring all have correct PPE for risks and enforcing any hearing protection zones.
- ☑ **Site deliveries** – managing any shared delivery areas, planning phased deliveries, using banksman, considering third parties and light levels.

**For further guidance refer to the corresponding GE 700 chapters, where applicable.**

*Operative working during fit out*

## Large shopfitting contract in a city

*Pedestrian and vehicle segregation in front of hoarding to control access and deliveries*

*Temporary works behind hoarding complete with working platforms*

*Planned road closures for a crane and lifting in a public space*

*Pre-planned access removed for steelwork delivery and fall arrest in use for slinger*

*Moving the steelwork into position*

*Removing the lifting equipment used to manoeuvre the steel into position*

## 4.4 Working at height

Almost every shopfitting project will involve the shopfitting contractor or their respective trade contractors in working at height. Statistics now clearly illustrate that working at height is a major cause of accidents.

Falls from height lead to serious injuries for all employees, including those in the shopfitting industry. This statement takes into consideration those employers who have manufacturing capability and wish to undertake routine maintenance on their properties, to shopfitting installation on a site owned by a third party.

*Full height barriers provide an internal safe zone by segregating the high risk façade replacement works*

The Work at Height Regulations encompass all work where a fall that is likely to cause injury may occur. The scope of the regulations includes all types of access equipment and work platforms, regardless of how long an employee is at height, or of the height at which the activity occurs.

The shopfitting industry, regardless of where the workplace is, includes the use of stepladders as a work platform for maintenance or other tasks, or simply as a means of accessing or leaving work at different levels.

Stepladders are not banned or illegal under the regulations. However, they should only be considered when all other safer alternatives for work at height have been ruled out when following the work at height hierarchy.

Due diligence in the form of a risk assessment must show that the task is of low risk and of short duration, or that there are features in the workplace that mean other equipment is not appropriate. If so, then ladders may be used. It should also be noted that stepladders come in many forms, some of which are safer than others, and include features such as adjustable out-riggers, platforms, handrails, lightweight GRP construction and tool tray attachments.

Lift shafts, new openings, strip out and removal of partitions, windows, façade, handrails, escalators and staircases create open edges that need to be controlled. The method statement must also consider how falls will be prevented while removing or reinstating these features.

*Temporary edge protection fixed into position*

Edge protection and fall prevention measures must be robust and secured into position, and again the method of installing these must include fall prevention. Plastic or free-standing barriers offer little resistance and a person can easily fall against and through them.

Falls from height are the most common cause of fatalities, accounting for almost a third of fatal injuries to workers.

The regulations require duty holders to ensure the following.

- ☑ All work at height is properly planned and organised.
- ☑ Those involved in work at height are competent.
- ☑ The risks from work at height are assessed and appropriate work equipment is selected and used.
- ☑ The risks from fragile surfaces are properly controlled.
- ☑ Equipment for work at height is properly inspected and maintained.

### 4.4.1 What constitutes work at height?

Work at height is work in any place, including a place at, above, or below ground level, where a person could be injured if they fell from that place. Access and egress to a place of work can also be deemed to be work at height. Below are some examples in a shopfitter's environment that can be classified as work at height.

- ☑ Working on any type of scaffolding.
- ☑ Work on a mobile elevating work platform.
- ☑ Being on the back of a lorry or raised loading bays.
- ☑ Working close to an excavation or a cellar opening (lift pit).
- ☑ Working off steps, hop ups and mobile towers.
- ☑ Mezzanine floors with no edge protection.
- ☑ Staircases with no handrails.
- ☑ Temporary wheelbarrow ramps onto the back of skips.
- ☑ Creating voids through floors or risers.

*Mobile towers, stepladders and MEWPs providing a typical range of access solutions*

**For further information on working at height refer to Chapters D01 to D05.**



## 4.5 Fire

Fire is an ever-present threat throughout the majority of construction and demolition projects. As shopfitting progresses, the nature of the fire risk is likely to change as different work starts and is completed. Therefore, not only must the risk of fire be managed continuously, but the management process must allow for the changing nature of the risk.

**For further guidance refer to Chapter C02 Fire prevention and control.**

### 4.5.1 Common sources of fire risk

- ☑ Storage and use of flammable materials, including LPG.
- ☑ Hot work.
- ☑ Arson.
- ☑ Smoking.
- ☑ Operating plant and equipment.
- ☑ Poor housekeeping.
- ☑ Electrical systems and equipment, including temporary lighting.

**It is vital that the project fire strategy takes into account all existing third-party fire arrangements.**

### 4.5.2 Specialist advice

The Fire Protection Association (FPA), in conjunction with the Construction Confederation (CC), published the eighth edition of *Fire prevention on construction sites* in July 2012. This joint Code of Practice (CoP) deals with the protection from fire on construction sites and buildings undergoing renovation.

The CoP does not have any legal status; however, it does outline good practice and many insurance companies now require that the authoritative guidelines (such as those detailed in the CoP) are properly implemented on construction projects before they will give full insurance.

The FPA also publishes *Construction site fire prevention checklist – a guide for insurers, surveyors and construction industry professionals.*

## 4.6 Health risks

The following topics must be considered when shopfitting and interior contracting. These are also covered in detail in other chapters.

### 4.6.1 Construction dust

Many shopfitting activities will give rise to dust, which should be considered as a high health risk.

Typical work that creates harmful levels of dust is shown below.

- ☑ Sweeping a dusty floor.
- ☑ Mechanically cutting, chasing or drilling concrete, bricks and blocks.
- ☑ Mixing sand and cement to make mortar.
- ☑ Sanding down MDF or timber.
- ☑ Rubbing down tape and jointing or plaster.

**All dusts are hazardous to health. The creation of dust, regardless of amount, must be controlled – all risk assessments and method statements should state how exposure to dust or fumes will be minimised. It is no longer acceptable to expect workers to work unprotected in dusty conditions.**

### Rubbing down tape and jointing

Traditionally rubbing down creates a lot of dust, which is both hazardous to health, has to be cleaned up and is manually intensive. This drywall sander with collection system minimises all these issues to the extent that the operative does not need RPE.

**For further guidance on how to manage dust and fumes, and to help check if method statements and risk assessments adequately address respiratory risks, refer to Chapter B10 Dust and fumes.**

## 4.6.2 Asbestos

Asbestos was widely used in the UK until it was banned in late 1999; disturbance of the fabric of any building built before this time has the potential to expose asbestos.

The requirements for licensed work remain the same: in the majority of cases, work with asbestos needs to be done by a licensed contractor. This work includes most asbestos removal, all work with sprayed asbestos coatings and asbestos lagging, and most work with asbestos insulation and asbestos insulating board (AIB).

- ☑ All asbestos-containing material (ACM) is hazardous when airborne and dangerous when fibres are inhaled.
- ☑ If you are carrying out non-licensed asbestos work, this still requires effective controls.
- ☑ Since 6 April 2012, some non-licensed work needs to be notified to the relevant enforcing authority.
- ☑ Since 6 April 2012, brief written records should be kept of non-licensed work, which has to be notified (such as a copy of the notification with a list of workers on the job), plus the level of likely exposure of those workers to asbestos. This does not require air monitoring on every job, if an estimate of degree of exposure can be made based on experience of similar past tasks or published guidance.
- ☑ Before any work that has the potential to expose anyone to asbestos is carried out, a survey must be carried out and a written risk assessment made.
- ☑ The priority for any employer is to prevent exposure to, and spread of, asbestos.
- ☑ A written, site-specific plan (or register) of work must be kept on site and followed.
- ☑ Anyone who does any work with asbestos must be specifically trained to do it, and this training must be repeated at least annually.
- ☑ Contractors producing hazardous asbestos waste must check that the site receiving the asbestos waste is authorised to receive asbestos. They should have an environmental permit.
- ☑ Be aware of other hazards that may arise from working with or managing asbestos (such as working at height, in a confined space or where the presence of live services must be managed).
- ☑ The Health and Safety Executive (HSE) must be notified:
  - of all work involving the disturbance of asbestos, apart from non-licensable work
  - separately, if the project is notifiable under the Construction (Design and Management) Regulations.
- ☑ The regulations require anyone who issues a site-clearance certificate to be accredited by an appropriate accreditation body as competent to carry out such work. In the UK the sole source of this accreditation is UKAS.

**For further information refer to Chapter B09 Asbestos.**

The Control of Asbestos Regulations require all those who may be exposed to asbestos to have appropriate asbestos awareness training.

### 4.6.3 Lead and lead-based paint

Old, lead-based paint is still likely to affect the majority of UK buildings. It was completely removed from general sale by 1992. As a result lead surveys are a mandatory requirement under the Construction (Design and Management) Regulations.

Exposure to lead, lead dust and fumes constitutes a major hazard to the health of those who work with lead, lead products and lead-containing materials (LCMs) (such as lead-based paint).

Lead paint and dust exposure risks are greatest within pre-1970 buildings and structures, especially during repair, maintenance, refurbishment and demolition, if proper precautions are not followed.

**For explanation on the risks and controls that are required when working with lead refer to Chapter B12 Lead.**



## 4.7 Supporting information

### 4.7.1 Guidance

*Shopfitter's guide to the Construction (Design and Management) Regulations.*

### 4.7.2 Code of Practice

*Code of Practice on the safe erection of hoardings and similar structures.*

*Code of Practice on manual handling in shopfitting.*

*Code of Practice on fire safety in the shopfitting industry.*

### 4.7.3 Shopfitting safely – a safe pair of hands now and in the future (DVD)

This health and safety induction DVD is for those who have entered, or are about to enter, the shopfitting and interior contracting environment as a member of the workforce. It is to help them understand the potential hazards that they are likely to be confronted with on site.

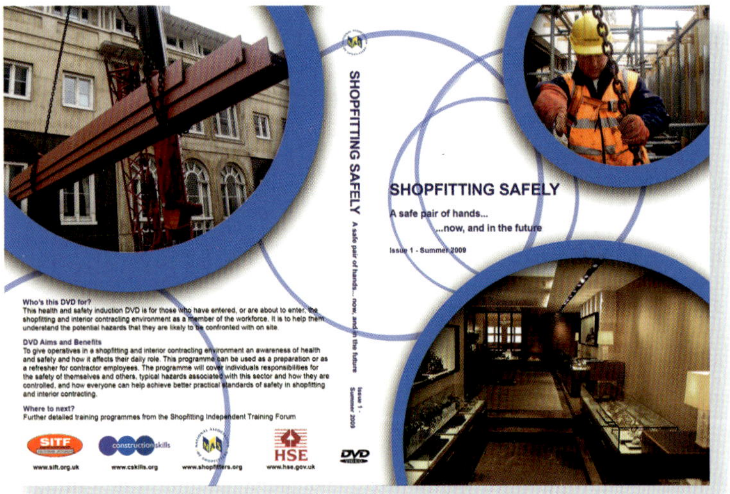


The DVD aims to give operatives in a shopfitting and interior contracting environment awareness of health and safety and how it affects their daily role. This programme can be used as a presentation or as a refresher for contractor employees. The programme will cover individuals' responsibilities for the safety of themselves and others, typical hazards associated with this sector and how they are controlled, and how everyone can help achieve better practical standards of safety.

## 4.7.4 Shopfitting safely – Occupational health and safety in a joinery workshop (DVD)

This DVD is for all people, in such an environment, to assist them to manage occupational health and safety risks effectively and positively.

The main elements contained in this DVD, to manage woodworking safely, include the following.

- ☑ **Risk management.** To reduce the chances of an accident occurring, it's best to look at what might cause one and then decide what you need to do to stop it happening.
- ☑ **Training and supervision.** By law, all workers must receive training and supervision that is appropriate to the equipment they will be using.
- ☑ **Workplace management.** Paying attention to layout, worker movement and keeping workshops and storage areas tidy can help reduce the risks. Workers themselves should also be encouraged to become involved in health and safety as they are often the best people to understand the risks and help find solutions.

Through worker involvement you can act together to reduce accidents and ill health within your manufacturing environment.

WWW.

**For further guidance, DVDs and copies of the appropriate codes refer to the National Association of Shopfitters.**

# 05

# Working over or near to water

## Contents



## Supporting information

### G: Checklists and forms

## Overview

**Where construction or demolition work takes place over or near to water, steps must be taken, primarily to stop anyone from falling into it, but also to ensure that someone who has fallen will not come to harm and can be promptly rescued.**

**When planning for safe working near to water, in addition to looking after the health and safety of employees, it may also be necessary to take into consideration the safety of the public, including those using the waterway, in areas where they still have access.**

**Tidal and fast flowing waters pose additional problems for anyone falling into them and their rescuers.**

**Whilst the word *water* will be used throughout this chapter, the dangers and precautions apply equally to where work is being carried out near to other liquids (such as slurries and chemicals in vats) and even free-flowing solids (such as foodstuffs in silos).**



## 5.1 Introduction

Managing and controlling the risks associated with working over or near to water is something that many managers will only do on rare occasions. This in itself could be a problem because they could be ill-prepared to do so when the need arises. The dangers in doing such work are significant and must be proactively managed.

Where construction and/or temporary works will block or partially block a navigable waterway, even on a temporary basis, it will be necessary to gain the permission of the navigation authority for that waterway during the planning stage.

The Health and Safety Executive (HSE) states that accidental drowning is often linked to one or more of the following factors.

- Failure to provide personal buoyancy equipment.
- Failure of personal buoyancy equipment to operate properly.
- Disregard for or misjudging the severity of the risks of getting it wrong.
- Lack of supervision, particularly of the young and inexperienced.
- Inability to cope once a problem arises.
- The absence of rescuers and rescue equipment.
- Failure to take account of weather forecasts.

Raising the awareness of managers, supervisors and workers to ensure effective control measures are always put in place and followed is fundamental to safe working over and near to water.

**Anyone who may accidentally fall into water will ideally be able to swim or at least feel sufficiently confident in their personal bouyancy equipment and the effectiveness of the rescue procedures, so that they do not panic.**

## 5.2 Important points

- Working over water will often, although not always, involve working at height. The potential risks arising from both hazards must be managed.
- The risks must be assessed and a written method statement produced.
- As with any other work at height, ideally it must be carried out from a stable working platform that will prevent an unplanned fall into the water; only as a last resort should fall-arrest equipment be relied upon.
- Where there is a risk of someone accidentally entering the water, appropriate rescue equipment and people who are competent to use it must be available.
- Appropriate personal protective equipment (PPE) must be made available.
- Instruction and training must be given to the workforce; suddenly falling fully clothed into cold, deep water may induce shock and an increased risk of drowning if appropriate PPE is not worn.
- Rescue drills must be planned and practised.
- Powered rescue boats must only be operated by someone trained in boat-handling and rescue procedures.
- If the use of a rescue boat is not appropriate, an established hierarchy of rescue methods must be followed.
- Working near to deep water (for example, adjacent to canal locks) can be as dangerous as working over water if appropriate control measures are not put in place.
- Potential health risks must also be managed.

**Would each of your workforce be at ease having fallen into water wearing a lifejacket, providing they were in no immediate danger?**

## 5.3 Risk management

### 5.3.1 Risk assessment

The risk assessment must investigate whether it is possible to eliminate the hazard of working over or near to water by doing the job another way. It is accepted that this will often not be possible. However, it may be possible to reduce the risks of falling and/or drowning by doing at least part of the job elsewhere. An example of this is the complete removal of lock-gates for off-site repair rather than doing the whole job with the gates in situ. The number of people exposed to the hazard, and the length of time they are exposed to it will both be significantly reduced.

*Safe access for the arrival and departure of site staff by waterborne transport*

As for all work, the significant risks arising out of doing the job, and the part they must play in seeing that the job is carried out safely, must be communicated to the workforce.

Where there is a risk of falling from a significant height into water and/or where the water is fast flowing or tidal the employer is advised to consider the selection of workers carefully. The HSE does not make any recommendations regarding whether anyone who runs the risk of falling into water must be able to swim, although it is obviously preferable that they can because they are more likely to be at ease in the water until rescued. A lifejacket will keep a non-swimmer afloat and automatically turn them face up.

The following points must be considered.

- ☑ Safe access to dry land, where people and materials are transported to site over the water.
- ☑ Site access by the emergency services and how an injured person is going to be transferred to an ambulance.



**For safety precautions that need to be observed when working over or near to water using an articulated boom mobile elevating work platform, refer to the HSE information sheet *Preventing falls from boom-type mobile elevating work platforms* (MISC614).**

### 5.3.2 Areas of risk

Hazardous work areas include the following.

*It is essential that fall prevention measures are taken, as for any other type of construction work*

- ☑ Docks and wharves.
- ☑ Locks.
- ☑ Canals and rivers, including bankside paths.
- ☑ Open sea (off-shore construction sites and installations).
- ☑ Lakes, reservoirs and ponds (natural and ornamental).
- ☑ Sewage and slurry ponds.
- ☑ Water-filled pits.
- ☑ Water-holding tanks, including those located underground.
- ☑ Culverts and other storm-drainage channels.

## 5.3.3 Hierarchy for working at height

As with any other work at height, when working over water the hierarchy of safety will be to avoid working at height (over water) if it is possible to do the job another way; prevent falls, if it is necessary to work at height; and minimise the personal trauma of anyone who does fall.

To avoid duplication, familiarise yourself with the content of other GE 700 chapters, some of which are likely to be relevant to working over water, in that they cover:

- ☑ scaffolds and other stable working platforms
- ☑ safe access using ladders
- ☑ the use of mobile elevating platforms
- ☑ fall prevention by harness and restraint lanyard
- ☑ fall arrest by harness and load-absorbing lanyard
- ☑ fall arrest by safety nets and soft-landing systems.

*A fully sheeted bridge scaffold, protecting the workforce and river users. (Note the rescue boat on the left bank)*

When working over water, scaffolds will often be cantilevered off the structure, slung underneath it or otherwise of a complex nature. People who are competent to do so must ensure they are:

- ☑ properly designed to be fit for purpose
- ☑ erected, modified, as necessary, and struck
- ☑ inspected, as necessary.



## 5.3.4 Preventing accidental entry into water

Every effort must be made to eliminate the risk of accidental entry into water. This will involve protecting employees against the following.

- ☑ Falls from heights (including a failure to use the fall prevention or arrest measures provided).
- ☑ Trips and slips from low level.
- ☑ Persons being knocked over by moving objects (for example, crane loads).
- ☑ Loss of balance (for example, caused by high winds) particularly when handling sheet materials.
- ☑ Failure or absence of barriers.
- ☑ Failure of ropes or lines.
- ☑ Rising swell or swell from passing waterborne traffic.
- ☑ Messing around.
- ☑ Being on site whilst under the influence of drink or drugs.

Site management must play an active part in ensuring that any of the above points that apply to their project, and others which may not be covered, are effectively managed.

## 5.3.5 Dangers from falling into water

The most immediate danger of accidental entry into water is drowning. The following could be causes or contributory factors.

- ☑ Shock of sudden immersion in cold water.
- ☑ Weight of waterlogged clothing.
- ☑ Incapacity following injury after striking an object during the fall or in the water.
- ☑ Fatigue or hypothermia where rescue is not immediate.

Other effects of falling, which importantly may render the victim incapable of assisting in their own rescue, include the following.

- Being knocked unconscious by hitting part of the structure during the fall.
- Suffering broken bones by hitting the structure during the fall.
- Suffering physical injury by falling into shallow water.

Risks to health include the following.

- Leptospirosis (Weil's disease) if infected rats are present.
- Digestive illnesses from swallowing water contaminated with natural organisms, chemicals used in the work process or other contaminants (such as diesel oil).
- Suffering suspension trauma by being left suspended in a harness for too long.

As soon as it is known that someone has fallen into the water, unless it is obvious that external medical assistance is not required, the emergency services should be called so that they are in transit whilst the rescue is being carried out.

## 5.4 Rescue equipment and procedures

Although every effort should be made to prevent people falling into the water, the risk of this happening may still remain. In the event of someone falling into water, three things are of paramount importance.

- The person must be kept afloat.
- Their location must be immediately obvious and continuously tracked, if in flowing water.
- Rescue must be achieved as quickly as possible.

**Getting an attempted rescue wrong could put the rescuers at risk.**

Methods of rescuing a casualty, other than by using a rescue boat, could include the following.

- **Involving the emergency services.** In many cases, the fire and rescue services (or coastguard in appropriate circumstances) will have the expertise and equipment to carry out rescue procedures. A judgement will have to be made as to whether it is advisable or practical to await their arrival. This must be balanced against the risks involved in attempting the following means of rescue.
- **Reaching out from the bank or edge.** If the casualty is near enough to the bank or edge, it may be possible to grab their hand, or use a sturdy stick, boat-hook, oar, broom handle, or anything they can seize to be pulled in to safety. Rescuers should ensure that they have a secure foothold and sufficient grip and balance to counteract the weight of the casualty in the water.
- **Throwing out a means of personal buoyancy.** When the casualty is some way out in the water, a lifebuoy and rescue line or any personal buoyancy aid with line attached should be thrown to them. This technique is preferable to entering the water to reach the casualty, especially if the depth of water and state of currents are not known.
- **Wading out.** A shelving bed or shore may enable rescuers to reach the person in the water while keeping their feet on the bottom. However, care should be taken as currents, underwater obstacles and sudden changes in the depth of water may put the rescuers at risk.
- **Going out.** Assistance should be summoned first when possible. Individuals should only act alone if they really have to. A boat should preferably be used to reach the casualty. If not, the rescuer should swim out with a lifeline secured to the shore or edge and a personal buoyancy aid.

**Avoid becoming a casualty. People who cannot swim should not enter the water, but must raise the alarm and wait for assistance.**

### 5.4.1 Personal buoyancy equipment

**Refer to the HSE information sheet *Personal buoyancy equipment on inland and inshore waters* (AIS1).**

Anyone working over or near to water, and at risk of falling in, should wear some form of personal buoyancy equipment; generally a lifejacket or buoyancy aid. Lifejackets and personal buoyancy aids are designed to keep the wearer afloat. There are, however, important differences and it is recommended that lifejackets are used in preference to buoyancy aids for reasons that are explained later in this chapter.

Decisions on the type of equipment best suited to specific types of work should be based on an assessment of the factors involved by the employer, which may have to consult suppliers in some circumstances. These may include, for example, whether a person is a competent swimmer, the length of time a person may be in the water, the risks of injury, water temperature, current and the proximity of assistance.

**Lifejackets** must be made to the relevant British Standard and must be obtained from a reputable supplier. Their primary aim is to support an unconscious person in the water by turning them face upwards. Inflation of the lifejacket is by means of a $CO_2$ cartridge, activated manually or automatically, depending upon the item purchased. Lifejackets that inflate automatically are preferable because:

- ☑ upon contact with the water the lifejacket will inflate within seconds and an unconscious person will be turned face upwards in the water
- ☑ with manually inflated lifejackets, not only must the wearer be capable of locating and pulling the manual inflation toggle, but the toggle can get caught on obstructions during normal work, inadvertently inflating the lifejacket.

Manually inflated lifejackets, which are inflated by mouth after entry into the water, should not be used.

**For advice on the selection of lifejackets and personal buoyancy aids refer to Appendix A.**

**Buoyancy aids** are intended to provide a conscious person with enough extra buoyancy to stay afloat and achieve a reasonable floating position. A basic buoyancy aid may not turn an unconscious person over from face down. Buoyancy is achieved by means of closed-cell foam pads sewn into the material of the buoyancy aid.

Buoyancy aids are bulky and, in some people's view, hinder movement and may slow the progress of work, in comparison to lifejackets, which offer greater freedom of movement.

Where a **safety harness** is to be worn in addition to personal buoyancy equipment, it is important to ensure each of these items is compatible, in that each will not interfere with the correct functioning of the other. Safety harness and buoyancy aid combinations are available from some manufacturers, although professional advice should be sought on their suitability for wearing during construction work before committing to them.

The provision of whistles and lights as aids to the location of people in the water may be advisable in some circumstances.

Wearers should be fully trained in the use of safety harnesses, lifejackets and personal buoyancy aids. The functions of the equipment and, where appropriate, its limitations should be clearly understood by users.

**The selection and care of personal buoyancy equipment are covered in Appendices A and B respectively.**

## 5.4.2 Lifebuoys

Lifebuoys should be available wherever people are working on, over or near to water. Standard 760 mm diameter lifebuoys with rope or cord lifelines (usually 30 m) attached should be placed in conspicuous positions near the water's edge.

A lifebuoy can be thrown only a short distance, perhaps six to eight metres and then with little accuracy.

Handling 30 m of rope may also present problems to the inexperienced person, although lifebuoys are available with the rope packed into plastic containers, from which it reels out when the lifebuoy is thrown.

Lifebuoys should be suspended from a suitable hook or bracket at a height where they can be clearly seen, with the lifeline coiled ready for use.

## 5.4.3 Rescue lines

Various types of rescue line (sometimes referred to as throwing lines) are available. Typically they comprise 20 or 30 m of rescue line enclosed within a canvas bag.

*A typical rescue line*

The free end of the line is held, while the bag is thrown underarm towards the casualty. The line can be delivered accurately up to its full length, but underarm throwing may be hindered by guard-rails and other forms of edge protection. Upon completion of the rescue, the line should be left extended to dry and it can then be repacked into the canvas bag when that has also dried.

The photo shows a typical rescue line with a loop tied in the free end to fit over the wrist. The bag, complete with the line, is then thrown to the person in the water, trailing the line as it goes. The particular line shown is equipped with a padded handle on the outside of the bag, which the person in the water will hold on to whilst they are pulled ashore.

Another method of delivering the line is the capsule emergency lifeline. A light but strong line, 40 m in length, is packed into a small plastic capsule. The free end of the line is secured to a cord grip that is held while the capsule is thrown, the line paying out as it goes.

The capsule may be thrown or flicked to the full distance of 40 m using an extension rod that fits into the handle. Both line and capsule will float, allowing the casualty to grab the line and be hauled to safety. If the first throw misses, it can be very quickly used again. The ability to deliver the line up to 40 m may avoid the need to launch a boat or for somebody to enter the water.

The capsules are small enough to be carried in a belt or, alternatively, can be mounted in cabinets (with the extension rod) at convenient locations.

Drownings have occurred close to the bank or water's edge. Safety provision should take account of this, where it is the dominant risk. Lightweight throwing lines or similar equipment should be provided to supplement lifebuoys, especially if workers are moving from place to place, adjacent to the water.

## 5.4.4 Stop nets or lines

As a pre-emptive measure and given the right circumstances, including still or gently flowing water and no waterborne traffic, stop nets may be suspended just into the water or lines trailed across or in the water to allow a conscious person to hold on while awaiting rescue, or to pull themselves to the bank. These cannot be totally relied upon, because a casualty may be unconscious or otherwise unable to help themselves.

If there is a weir or sluice, stop nets or lines should not be relied upon unless they can be positioned well upstream of it.

## 5.4.5 Rescue nets

Recovering a fully dressed person from the water into a rescue boat can be very difficult, particularly if there is a heavy swell and/or they are unconscious or injured and therefore unable to assist in their own rescue.

*Rescue net extended over decking for illustrative purposes*

Rescue nets, which clip to fittings along one side of a rescue boat, have been developed to assist in such rescues.

Requirements for a rescue net are shown below.

- ☑ When not required it should be clipped in a roll and stored in the boat.
- ☑ When required for a rescue it should be lowered into the water with the rescue boat crew keeping hold of the outer edge.
- ☑ Slight negative buoyancy, enabling the rescue boat crew to slide the person into the water, supported by their lifejacket, over the net.
- ☑ Equipped with handles and loops to enable the person in the water to be gently hauled over the side of the rescue boat.

## 5.4.6 Rescue boats

A risk assessment will identify if a rescue boat should be provided whenever work is taking place over or near to deep, tidal or fast flowing water. It will also be necessary to provide a rescue boat in some situations where work is carried out above or close to still water (for example, where high, steep banks and the absence of self-rescue ladders prevent the person in the water effecting their own rescue).

Any rescue boat must comply with the regulations and byelaws of the navigation authority in whose waters it is operating.

The craft may be rigid (wooden or fibreglass) or inflatable. It must have a reliable engine and carry the following, depending on the findings of the risk assessment.

*A typical powered rescue boat, equipped with radio, throwing line, paddles, boat-hook and a first-aid box*

- ☑ A radio, if they are being used on site, or a working mobile phone.
- ☑ A first-aid kit.
- ☑ Paddles, in case of engine failure.
- ☑ A boat-hook.
- ☑ A throwing line.
- ☑ Grab-lines around the hull.
- ☑ A rescue net.

The boat crew should be experienced and competent at handling the rescue craft on appropriate waterways, particularly in rescue situations that involve special boat-handling skills.

**Where a powered rescue boat will be used it is strongly recommended that the operator is trained to a minimum standard of Royal Yachting Association (RYA) Power Boat Level 2 and also in rescue techniques. Rescuing a person from the water in a power boat with a rotating propeller demands skill and experience, particularly if there is a current flowing and/or strong winds. Ideally, there will be two people in the boat, the driver and a rescuer.**

**The RYA runs courses throughout the United Kingdom.**

Whether the rescue boat is to be permanently manned and constantly afloat or not will depend on the circumstances, as will its size and the equipment to be carried. If any work is to be done during the hours of darkness, the rescue boat will require high efficiency lighting.

Two-way radio communication between boat and shore may be necessary on large areas of water. Practice rescue drills should be held, so that the best method of rescuing, securing and landing a potential casualty is known in advance.

**It is advisable for practice drills to be carried out and people on site made aware of the emergency arrangements.**

### Kill cords

*The kill cord must be clipped around the driver's leg or to their lifejacket*

It is essential that powered rescue boats are equipped with a kill cord, which will stop the engine if the driver falls overboard or otherwise moves from the driving position. A driverless power boat, particularly if on full lock so that it drives itself around in circles whilst people are in the water, is very dangerous.



## 5.5 Onshore facilities and procedures

**First aid.** Irrespective of the size of the operation, first-aid facilities must be provided, and trained and qualified first aiders should be present at the site of all work adjacent to water.

Facilities should include provision for transferring casualties from boat to shore and ambulance access.

**Alarms.** Some effective means of raising an alarm must exist. Gongs, bells, whistles, pressurised canister fog horns, klaxons or similar items of equipment should be provided. All people on site should be instructed in the correct use of the alarm and the actions to be taken when the alarm sounds.

**Lighting.** Water surfaces should be illuminated at night so that victims of falls can be seen and constantly watched while awaiting rescue.

**Communications.** The telephone number for the ambulance, coastguard and lifeboat services (999) should be stressed to operatives and adequate provision should be made for effective on-site communications (usually site radios).

**Rescue equipment** is for use in an emergency. It must be properly maintained, not misused and never relied upon as a primary safeguard against accidents.

**Clothing.** High-visibility vests or jackets should be worn. These will assist in keeping the casualty in view while the rescue operation is being mounted. High-visibility immersion suits will be appropriate in some circumstances.

**Checking personnel.** Periodic checks should be made to ensure nobody is missing. Personnel should work in pairs or in sight of each other to enable one person to raise the alarm in the event of an emergency.

**Weather and tides.** Details of weather and, where appropriate, tides should be obtained before each shift.

**Safety ladders.** Where there is a quay-heading to the bank, there is likely to be a significant height difference between the water level and the dry land, which can make it difficult or impossible for someone who is fully dressed in wet clothes to clamber out of the water. Safety ladders can be made by cutting good sections out of damaged aluminium ladders, which are then fixed to the quay-heading, using suitable metal brackets, as an easy means of getting back on to the bank.

**Recovery of equipment from the water.** In the event of tools, equipment or small plant falling into the water, no attempt should be made to recover those using amateur divers or improvised techniques.

Special regulations apply to all diving operations and expert advice should be sought where it is necessary to recover equipment.

## 5.6 Training

Safe working practices and rescue procedures must be covered during site induction, refresher training and any specialist training.

A clearly defined and documented rescue procedure should be devised. All on site must be familiar with the procedure and understand the actions they must take in an emergency.

The location of emergency equipment should be known and any special training in its use given to the personnel involved. Responsibility for co-ordinating and supervising rescue operations must be allocated to identify individuals, trained and competent to discharge it. Practices in rescue procedures should be held where appropriate.

Locally employed site-based staff and the employees of sub-contractors should receive instruction in emergency procedures and the use of life-preserving equipment, and must be given such information as is necessary to enable them to act effectively in an emergency.

With regard to personal buoyancy equipment, all workers who are likely to use it must be trained in the following.

- ☑ Adjust the securing straps to make sure it will not come off over the head, upon impact with water.
- ☑ Check that the firing mechanism of a lifejacket has not already been activated.
- ☑ Carry out pre-use and routine maintenance checks.
- ☑ Store the equipment correctly when not in use, particularly if it is wet.
- ☑ Appreciate any limitations in its use or performance.
- ☑ Report suspected or actual defects and obtain a replacement item if necessary.

## Appendix A – Selection of lifejackets

Lifejackets are divided into different categories of buoyancy. The criterion of each class is the support (personal buoyancy) provided by each category, which is expressed in Newtons (N).

The European Union standards that cover lifejackets also require a level of protection for the unconscious person in the water. This means that lifejackets must distribute the weight of the wearer in such a manner that the person is turned face up. The standards require that automatic lifejackets must self-inflate within 10 seconds of contact with water.

The personal buoyancy level in the standards relate to a person weighing 70 kg, thus the amount of actual personal buoyancy provided by any lifejacket will depend upon the weight of the wearer.

Consider the following situations.

- ☑ Wearing a lifejacket with too little personal buoyancy poses obvious problems as there may be too little support for a heavy person to keep their face out of the water or possibly even turn them face up if unconscious.
- ☑ Conversely, wearing a lifejacket with too much personal buoyancy could also pose problems; wearers who are not particularly heavy will be more buoyant and, for example, could find it difficult to escape from an air pocket if they have to fully immerse themselves and their lifejacket to duck under an obstruction.

The selection of the most appropriate lifejacket is therefore essential.



### 50 N personal buoyancy aid

For use by good swimmers in safe water only as long as assistance is at hand. Not safe for unconscious persons.

### 100 N lifejacket

Suitable for adults who are swimmers and for use in inland waters and safe areas, providing limited protection for unconscious persons depending upon the clothing worn.

### 150 N lifejacket

Suitable for swimmers and non-swimmers in all waters. Only limited protection for unconscious persons wearing heavy waterproof clothing or in heavy seas.

### 275 N lifejacket

For offshore use and extreme conditions. Immediate protection for unconscious persons, with turnover guaranteed in five seconds. Adequate personal buoyancy even in heavy clothing.

## Appendix B – Caring for personal buoyancy equipment

### Pre-use checks

**These must be carried out each time an item of personal buoyancy equipment is used.**

Inspecting personal buoyancy aids is relatively simple with regard to looking for defects in the securing straps, zips, seams and fabric.

Inspecting a lifejacket is slightly more complex and should be carried out in accordance with the manufacturer's instructions. It will normally include visual checks to ensure:

- ☑ the firing mechanism has not been activated (this is usually made obvious by the fact that the lifejacket is found inflated)
- ☑ the automatic firing capsule and gas cylinder are correctly screwed in place
- ☑ there are no signs of corrosion, cracks or dents in the gas cylinder or automatic firing capsule
- ☑ unwanted movement within the firing mechanism (creepage) has not occurred.

Some automatic inflation mechanisms have colour coded indicators to show when compression in the spring has been lost. Those that do not have such indicators will require careful inspection to judge whether the spring has lost any compression. Examination of the piston or other visible component may also show whether creepage has happened.

The user must make sure that the:

- ☑ whistle and light (when fitted) are in position
- ☑ oral inflation tube is capped
- ☑ straps and main body of the jacket are not worn or damaged
- ☑ inflatable bladder of the lifejacket is correctly packed in accordance with the manufacturer's instructions, ensuring that any Velcro is correctly fastened and the manual inflation lanyard is easy to get to.

Where damage to a personal buoyancy device is discovered, unless it is to be discarded and replaced, it must be returned to the manufacturer or its appointed agent for repair. Local repairs should not be attempted.

### Routine maintenance

The routine maintenance of lifejackets must be carried out in accordance with the manufacturer's instructions, in addition to pre-wear checks. As a general guide, where lifejackets are used daily, it is recommended that inspections are carried out at least monthly. However, where lifejackets are used in more harsh conditions (for example, off shore) the periods between inspections may need to be more frequent.

Inspection and testing must be carried out by those competent in recognising defects and the remedial action to be taken. Records must be kept of all inspections and repairs carried out.

Testing the air-tightness of the lifejacket will involve orally inflating the lifejacket and leaving it overnight (or submerging it in water) to check for leaks. The automatic inflation mechanism must be dismantled to make a detailed examination of its condition.

As part of the maintenance inspection, further checks are shown below.

- ☑ All screw threads must be examined for signs of rust. Rust can lead to problems in locating the cocking cap or keeping the gas cylinder in the correct position.
- ☑ The gas cylinder must be examined for corrosion, cracks, dents and other defects. Particular attention must be paid to the cylinder cap as any indentations found could mean that the automatic firing mechanism has fired but failed to pierce the cylinder. If this is the case, the reason for activation and the cause of failure needs to be identified.
- ☑ The cylinder fitting and groove of the firing pin must be checked to ensure that they are free from dirt.
- ☑ The automatic inflation mechanism must be operated manually (with the gas cylinder removed) to ensure that it operates smoothly, and that there is no obstruction to the movement of the pin that prevents it piercing the cylinder. The firing pin must be checked to ensure that it is sharp.
- ☑ The salt or paper ring must be inspected for any cracking, dissolving or tearing that has taken place since the last inspection.
- ☑ Where fitted, the rubber 'O' ring must be inspected for damage and that it is correctly seated.
- ☑ The mechanism must be checked for signs of creepage.

Once the inspection is complete, the lifejacket should be reassembled according to the manufacturer's instructions.

## Servicing

The servicing of each lifejacket should be carried out by the manufacturer or their appointed agents, every two years. However, where lifejackets are used regularly and in harsh conditions, an annual or more frequent service may be needed.

## Management

A clear policy on the use, inspection and storage of automatically inflated lifejackets must be in place. This policy also addresses the training needs of the lifejacket users.

Lifejackets, if used regularly, should be allocated to individual users. Each individual, having been adequately trained, can then be responsible for carrying out pre-wear checks and inspections, and report defects according to company procedures. This will help ensure that correct inflation of the lifejackets is not jeopardised by the carelessness of others.

Management must enforce its policy on lifejackets. This can be achieved by spot checks of both the condition of the lifejackets in use and the records of inspection and servicing.

## Storage

Personal floatation equipment must be stored in dry conditions when not in use. Exposure to damp, humid conditions can lead to deterioration in the automatic inflation mechanism, known as creepage. This has the potential to lead to failure of the pin to pierce the carbon dioxide gas cylinder.

Lifejackets must be stored in dry conditions. The following advice should be observed when storing lifejackets.

- ☑ Do not hang lifejackets in contact with wet oilskins or other damp clothing; make sure there is enough space around them to allow the air to circulate.
- ☑ If a lifejacket is wet, unpack it and leave it to dry out on a hanger.
- ☑ Do not store lifejackets close to or directly above heat sources (such as convection heaters).
- ☑ To prevent water getting into the automatic inflation mechanism, do not store wet lifejackets upside down or lying flat.

# 06

# Mobile workforce and driver safety

## Contents



## Supporting information

### G: Checklists and forms

## Overview

**The description of a mobile workforce covers a multitude of trades in many different situations from, for example, a lone worker called out to an emergency, with little knowledge and control, to work in an unfamiliar or hostile environment where potentially customer or client control is minimal.**

**This chapter provides a general overview of the legal framework and some practical guidance on the management of health and safety at work for mobile, lone and out-of-hours workers; the potential risks they may be exposed to; and practical advice on the management and control of their work.**

## 6.1 Introduction

This chapter aims to provide employers and managers with general practical guidance on processes and controls that can be put in place to provide their workers with a safe place of work. This ranges from simply saying 'tell us where you are' to planned work that identifies mobile locations where permits may be required.

Management preparation information, pre-job briefing, competence, self-discipline, control, awareness and training are also identified, all of which will form a package of safety for the mobile workforce.

**Employers have responsibility for the health, safety and welfare at work of all of their employees. These responsibilities cannot be transferred to any other person, including those people who work alone. It is the employer's duty to assess risks to lone workers and take steps to eliminate or control risks where necessary.**



The types of workers covered within this chapter are mobile groups of workers (gangs), lone and out-of-hours workers.

### Types of workers

- Mobile groups of workers.
  - A group of operatives working away from their home base, undertaking such work as, for example, domestic and small scale commercial refurbishment. This can include painters and decorators, scaffolders and roof workers.
  - Gangs of workers undertaking minor road works *(refer to Chapter F01 Street works and road works)* and rail maintenance works *(refer to Chapter F02 Trackside safety)*.
  - Those working in areas accessed by the general public to do work for the utility companies (gas, electric, water and telecommunications).
- Lone workers.
  - This group will include maintenance workers (such as plumbers, electricians, lift engineers, water and gas specialists, domestic aerial installers, aerial and mast maintenance personnel, and many others).
- Out-of-hours workers.
  - Those identified as mobile groups of workers or lone workers may, in addition, be required to work out of normal working hours to ensure continuance of 24-hour operations (for example, utility companies – gas, water, electricity and telecommunications).

## 6.2 Important points

### 6.2.1 Groups of workers

- Assess the risks to the mobile workers for that particular environment and the tasks to be undertaken.
- Ensure there has been consultation to ensure all relevant hazards have been considered.
- Employers with five or more employees have to record significant findings of risk assessments.
- Ensure there is a scheme of work in place prior to work commencing.
- Provide the supervisor with means to update risk assessment at the scene (such as point of work risk assessment).
- Verify they have a suitable level of training and competency (such as CSCS, PASMA and trade qualifications).
- Decide on equipment needed. Are special transport arrangements required?
- Ensure the vehicle is suitable for the number of personnel to be carried.

- ☑ Ensure the vehicle is appropriate if required to tow equipment (such as mini digger, trailer or welfare unit).
- ☑ Ensure the vehicle is rated for the safe towing weight limit.
- ☑ Consider safe access to roof of vehicle (such as mechanised roof access), if it is unavoidable that equipment will need to be carried (such as ladders and pipes).
- ☑ Avoid climbing on or off flatbed lorries during deliveries, consider use of pallets, loads pre-slung for mechanical means to avoid inertia reels on gallows, and so on.
- ☑ Does the area need segregation from pedestrians or from other traffic during deliveries?
- ☑ Is temporary traffic lighting and street signage needed? *(Refer to Chapter F01 Street works and road works.)*

- ☑ Is a fire emergency plan in place, including details of actions to take, assembly point, audible warning device and fire extinguishers?
- ☑ Ensure the work area is secure, including storage of materials, suitable waste containers, and so on.
- ☑ Consider what welfare arrangements are needed for these works, provision of an integral welfare unit that complies with Health and Safety Executive (HSE) requirements (refreshment/seating area, toilet, shower, clothes storage and drying, generator), use of client's facilities (with written agreement) or public facilities within suitable proximity.
- ☑ Do the works require an emergency rescue plan in situ – are they high risk, confined space, work at height or electrical?
- ☑ Has a first-aid kit been provided, suitable for the number of persons and risks present?
- ☑ Is a member of the group trained either as an appointed person or trained first aider, depending on the outcome of the first aid needs assessment. *(Refer to Chapter B05 First aid.)*
- ☑ Have suitable receptacles been provided to store waste for removal to suitable disposal facilities?

## 6.2.2 Lone workers

The following points are additional to the relevant items mentioned above.

- ☑ Does the lone worker require extra risk control measures (such as a personal alarm or mobile phone)?
- ☑ Ensure training in completion of point of work risk assessment.
- ☑ Does the workplace present a specific risk to the lone worker (such as vulnerable tenants or working at height)?
- ☑ Is there a safe way in and out of the premises for one person?
- ☑ Can any necessary temporary access equipment (such as portable ladders or trestles) be safely handled by one person?
- ☑ Can all the machinery and goods involved in the workplace be safely handled by one person?
- ☑ Are any chemicals or hazardous substances being used that may pose a risk to the worker?
- ☑ Does the work involve lifting objects too large for one person?
- ☑ Is more than one person needed to operate essential controls for the safe running of equipment or workplace transport?
- ☑ Is there a risk of violence?
- ☑ Are young, pregnant or disabled workers particularly at risk if they work alone and is a further specific risk assessment required?
- ☑ Are there any other reasons why the individual (for example, on medication) may be more vulnerable than others?
- ☑ Are emergency contact arrangements in place in case of an incident (such as regular reporting to supervisor, GPS systems/ tracker, regular phone contact, monitoring of staff security systems and so on)?

## 6.2.3 Out-of-hours workers

Either lone workers or groups of workers may need to work out of hours, frequently at short notice, therefore the following points also apply, in addition to those above.

- ☑ Are arrangements made for emergency situations (such as who to contact and backup information)?
- ☑ Has a specific risk assessment been completed?
- ☑ Has the operative been provided with method statements for tasks to be undertaken?
- ☑ Do they have the correct equipment required, and can it be managed by the operative(s)?

## 6.3 Legislative requirements

Many pieces of legislation are applicable to these types of workers – some of these are listed below.

- **Health and Safety at Work Act** – the umbrella Act under which most health and safety regulations have evolved. For example, it details information regarding an employer's duties in the workplace, about access and egress, provision and suitability of plant provision, information instruction supervision and training of personnel, an employee's duties and much more. *(For further information refer to Chapter A01 Health and safety law.)*
- **Management of Health and Safety Regulations** – risk assessments and controls, monitoring and review. *(For further information refer to Chapter A05 Risk assessments and method statements.)*
- **Provision and Use of Work Equipment Regulations** – testing and maintenance information (such as chainsaw, angle grinder and compressor). *(For further information refer to Chapter C05 Plant and work equipment.)*
- **Lifting Operations and Lifting Equipment Regulations** – cranes, telehandlers, lorry-loaded cranes and lifting accessories, including testing and maintenance requirements. *(For further information refer to Chapter C07 Lifting operations, and Chapter C08 Lifting equipment.)*
- **Construction (Design and Management) Regulations** – provides guidance for welfare arrangements. *(For further information refer to Chapter A03 Construction (Design and Management) Regulations.)*
- **Work at Height Regulations** – provides information on scaffolding, use of ladders and alternative means of working safely at height. *(For further information refer to Chapter D01 Work at Height Regulations.)*
- **Personal protective equipment** – information on legislative requirements, for example types and uses of specific equipment (such as goggles and dust masks) in particular environments and training in the fitting of such items. *(For further information refer to Chapter B06 Personal protective equipment.)*

F 06

## 6.4 Risk assessment and control

**A risk assessment is an important step in protecting your workers and your business, as well as complying with the law. It helps you focus on the risks that really matter in your workplace – the ones with the potential to cause real harm.**

**For further information on the risks of working alone refer to the HSE guidance.**

### 6.4.1 Assessing and controlling the risk

Employers need to investigate the potential hazards faced by workers and assess the risks involved both to these workers and to any person(s) who may be affected by their work. Employers should ensure that measures are in place to control or avoid such risks.

Where the risk assessment shows that it is not possible for the work to be done safely by an identified lone worker, arrangements for providing help or backup should be put in place.

The risk assessment must also identify the level of supervision required. High risk activities may require another person to be present (for example, if visiting a vulnerable tenant or for high risk confined space working).

### 6.4.2 Employer responsibilities

- **Involve** staff or their representatives when undertaking the required risk assessment process.
- Take steps to **check control measures** are in place (examples of control measures include instruction, training, supervision and issuing protective equipment).
- **Review** risk assessments annually or, as few workplaces stay the same, when there has been a significant change in working practice.
- When a risk assessment shows it is not possible for the work to be conducted safely by a lone worker, address that risk by, for example, making arrangements to **provide help or back-up**.
- Where a lone worker is working at another employer's workplace, that employer should **inform the lone worker's employer** of any risks and the required control measures.

**Refer to the HSE publication *Five steps to risk assessment* (INDG163).**

## 6.4.3 Point of work risk assessment

A risk assessment completed by the employer or supervisor should be provided to the workforce prior to any works commencing on site where practicable. However, there are many occasions when a point of work risk assessment will be required.

- ☑ To update the previously prepared risk assessment.
- ☑ As a result of changes to the working environment.
- ☑ As a result of changes to the works to be undertaken.
- ☑ For out-of-hours working, when each call out will require a specific risk assessment (for example, emergency maintenance (such as a serious water leak/flooding), urgent utilities works (such as a gas leak or explosion)).
- ☑ For a maintenance worker who is undertaking a number of different calls in a day where generic information is available but needs to be tailored to a specific task.

On arrival at site report to the person on site, contact base to confirm arrival (lone worker safety protocol) and prepare a point of work risk assessment.

**Employers and supervisors must satisfy themselves that the workforce is competent to carry out a point of work risk assessment. Training should be provided that includes practical, on-site mentoring.**

**If a site activity *cannot* be done safely, the workforce must know when *not to start* and contact the supervisor for further advice.**

Some examples of unsafe working areas and/or conditions are shown below.

- ☑ An unguarded excavation.
- ☑ Traffic not segregated.
- ☑ Permits to work and disconnections and isolations where certificates do not match.
- ☑ Scaffolding where inspection records are not present or the date has expired.
- ☑ Inadequate or wrong equipment and lack of training on the equipment.
- ☑ No fire extinguisher.
- ☑ Incorrect tools.
- ☑ Inadequate and/or unsuitable PPE.

### 6.4.3.1 Filling in a point of work risk assessment

- ☑ **Part 1. Stop** and ensure the area is safe with adequate access and egress. Complete items listed under this section. Seek advice from a supervisor if you answer **no** to any of them.
- ☑ **Part 2. Think** about what hazards may be present and carry out a safety assessment of those identified. Determine if the existing controls are adequate. Provide brief details of your rescue plan for safe escape in the event of something going wrong. Make a note on the form of any hazards that are significant but without, or with insufficient, controls.
- ☑ **Part 3. Act.** Detail additional hazards and control measures needed to manage the risk. Is the remaining risk acceptable for work to commence? If no, this needs input from your supervisor.
- ☑ **Part 4. Review,** and inform your supervisor if the job created any additional hazards, also if there are lessons to be learned.

**For further information refer to the example in Section G: *Checklists and forms.***

## 6.5 Welfare facilities for mobile workers

Health and safety legislation requires that welfare arrangements for projects of any size are pre-arranged prior to works commencing on site. For these circumstances there are two types to be considered.

1. Use of client's facilities – pre-arranged and confirmed in writing, or local public convenience.
2. Provision of an integrated hygiene unit, which complies with HSE requirements and includes refreshment area, toilet, drying area and generator.

If local facilities or a portaloo are considered sufficient then van-mounted equipment could be used for washing and preparation of food and refreshment, using a battery-mounted inverter.

**e.g.** **Mobile work vans fitted out with welfare facilities**

Refer to the *Provision of welfare facilities during construction work* Construction information sheet (CIS) 59.

## 6.6 Waste storage and disposal

Waste that is created at a site must be disposed of appropriately. Hazardous waste will need to be stored in appropriate containers and removed by licensed contractors using waste transfer notes.

Non-hazardous waste generated during works undertaken by mobile groups of workers or lone workers can be transported to their base for sorting and transferring to suitable recycling facilities or landfill sites.

The following points will need to be considered.

- ☑ Is the waste suitable for transporting? Is it hazardous or non-hazardous, and does it require special handling?
- ☑ Is the person planning to remove it competent to do so?
- ☑ Has the waste been segregated (for example, plasterboard separated from electrical)?
- ☑ Can the waste be segregated in the vehicle, by bagging, being placed in enclosed containers or requiring collection from the location?
- ☑ Do the mobile workers have suitable materials to package the waste products?
- ☑ Can the waste be carried without exceeding the safe working load of the vehicle?

**If using a company vehicle to carry waste back to a depot or to a licenced waste treatment or disposal facility, then a waste carrier's licence may be required.**

For further information refer to Chapter E03 Waste management.

## 6.7 Driver safety

The majority of jobs involve an element of driving, be it to or from work, between sites or operating plant. The HSE has made it clear that health and safety law applies to driving at work. Therefore, employers have a responsibility to ensure they have considered work-related road risks and implemented the necessary controls.

**For details of safe driving and work-related road risk refer to Appendix A.**

### 6.7.1 Drowsy driving

Another factor to consider is the effects of driving when drowsy.

The vast majority of people believe that drowsy driving is unacceptable, yet the incidence of drowsy driving suggests there is a disconnect between what people say and what they do. Depending on which piece of research you read, between 20% and 40% of all accidents on the road are attributable to fatigue.

Companies should encourage a healthy work-life balance and be alert to signs of driver fatigue.

Research has been undertaken to investigate the costs and understand the signs associated with drowsy driving, and to provide strategies to prevent it and explain how organisations can counter the problem.

**For further information refer to the Third Pillar of Health website.**

# Appendix A – Safe driving and work-related road risk

## Prospect guide

The following guidance has been reproduced with the kind permission of Prospect, the trade union for professionals.

This guidance is aimed at managers and professionals to give a balanced view of what employers should do, what employees should do and what managers should do as both an employee and representative of the employer.

www. **This health and safety guidance can be downloaded from the Prospect website.**

## Introduction

### Fact

Being killed in a car crash is the greatest risk most Prospect members/managers will ever face.

### Risk control

Requires **your employer and you** to share responsibility for:

- ☑ your organisation's driving policy, culture and performance
- ☑ the vehicle you use
- ☑ the journey you make
- ☑ how you drive
- ☑ the ergonomics: your interface with the vehicle.



### Aims

This guidance aims to:

- ☑ safeguard you as a road user
- ☑ protect you as a duty holder
- ☑ enable Prospect representatives to measure and promote their employer's compliance.

## 1.0 Driven to death

It's a tragedy when anyone is killed or maimed on the road. But it's even worse when they were simply trying to do their job, especially if it turns out their workload was overstretching them.

Around 1,000 road deaths and 13,000 serious road injuries every year are work related.

The facts are that:

- ☑ up to one in three crashes involves a vehicle being driven for work
- ☑ every week, around 200 road deaths and serious injuries involve someone at work
- ☑ research suggests, company car drivers who drive at least once a week are 40-50% more likely to have an incident.

These figures include road users driving for a living (such as road haulage and delivery drivers). However, studies of drivers with **high work-related mileage** (be that for work or long car journeys after work) demonstrate that they tend to have an elevated accident rate and to drive while **fatigued**, under time **pressure** and **distracted** by in-car tasks.

**These risk factors are clearly relevant to Prospect members/managers.**

## 2.0 The regulatory framework

The significance of work-related road deaths is rarely highlighted by the Health and Safety Executive, because primary enforcement of road traffic law is the responsibility of the police, not the HSE. But this doesn't eradicate the health and safety requirements on the employer to control and manage work-related road risk, alongside other occupational risks.

www. **To this end, HSE and the Department for Transport have published *Driving at work: managing work-related road safety* to assist.**

In recent years many employers have significantly enhanced their precautions and safety checks. This may have been prompted by the insurance industry telling employers to be more defensive, to address the rise in insurance claims; or it may be because of the introduction of the Corporate Manslaughter and Corporate Homicide Act, when it was widely expected that the police would prosecute companies for work-related road fatalities.

However, many companies still focus on driver-centred interventions (such as selection and training). They pay scant attention to the day-to-day working practices and pressures that mean their staff drive thousands of business miles a year, often at peak times, against deadlines and with the expectation that they will respond to work-related phone calls.

**Drivers often feel compelled to divide their attention between driving and an imminent meeting or task. This is dangerous and undermines both employer and driver compliance with the law.**

## 3.0 The law in brief

Work-related road risk is no different from any other work-related risk: the employer has common law duties of care and statutory duties under the Health and Safety at Work Act and its associated regulations.

**So health and safety management duties on policy, risk assessment, maintenance, staff training, monitoring and auditing apply equally. This is required by the Management of Health and Safety at Work Regulations and the Provision and Use of Work Equipment Regulations, because a car is included as work equipment.**

Typically, success requires commitment from the top, employee consultation and involvement (to ensure shared ownership) and proper policy implementation by line management. It also requires you, as an employee, to adhere to the standards that are agreed and to report any problems that arise in the course of your work.

After all, there may be a flaw or something impractical in the policy or procedure that you are meant to follow which, if left uncorrected, is subsequently held against you as the basis for non-compliance.

**So, if you spot a problem, report it!**

| Your employer | You |
|---|---|
| Create a safe driving culture that staff supports | ■ Ensure a workable driving policy<br>■ Report known deficiencies |
| Ensure vehicle suitability and road worthiness | ■ Maintain own vehicle<br>■ Check pool/hire/supply car |
| Ensure driver fitness, competence and compliance | ■ Comply with road traffic law |
| Set realistic meeting times and journeys | ■ Agree realistic meeting times and journeys |

This members' guide considers the law in practice: what your employer should be doing to assess and manage the risks, what you as a driver can do to help yourself, and some of the case law that highlights how everyone has responsibilities. Reps can use the questions listed as a basis for monitoring, negotiating and as always, making a difference.

**For more details of specific statutory requirements, members should refer to government sources kept up to date electronically, such as the websites provided by GOV.UK, the Driver and Vehicle Licensing Agency and the HSE.**

## 4.0 Assessing the risks

Driving is arguably one of the most skilled and demanding tasks we undertake. Drivers must control their vehicle while taking account of and reacting to the constantly changing environment. This requires sustained attention, vigilance, decision making, memory and perceptual motor skills.

Risk assessment for driving is no different from any other risk assessment. It's about the hazards that can cause harm, who could be injured or killed and the likelihood or chance of this happening.

Your employer should have a generic risk assessment for the driving typically expected in the course of its business and which takes account of the vehicle, driver and journey. More specific risk assessments may be required in circumstances that go outside the general norm: for instance, in the event of a serious deterioration in the weather.

## Key considerations of generic risk assessment

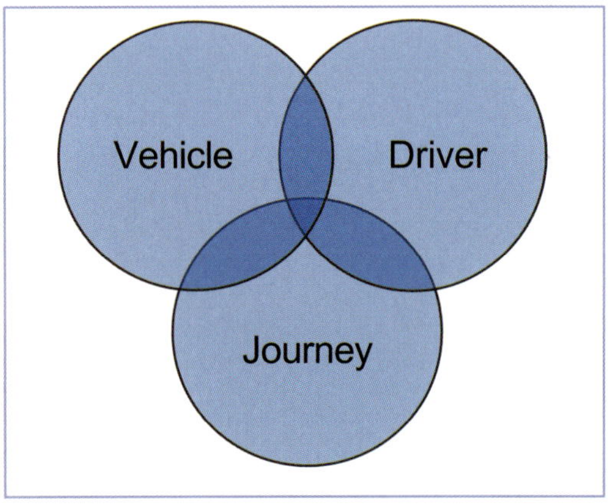


The questions that follow are those that employers should cover in their driving policy and/or generic risk assessment. Most are reproduced from guidance jointly developed by the HSE and the Department for Transport. Prospect reps and members can use them as a checklist, to benchmark employer compliance.

### Vehicle suitability – Is it fit for purpose?

☑ Do you take account of ergonomic considerations before purchasing or leasing new vehicles? According to the HSE, people who drive more than 25,000 miles a year have far more sick leave than low-mileage drivers. A good proportion is likely to be 'repetitive driving injury', such as back or neck pain, as a result of poor driving posture.

☑ Do you ensure that privately owned vehicles are not used for work unless they are insured for business use and, where applicable, have an MOT?



### Vehicle condition – Are vehicles safe and fit?

☑ Do you have suitable planned preventive maintenance arrangements? How do you verify standards are met? Are you clear about who has responsibility for vehicle checks, when and to what extent? (This includes fleets and rentals.)

☑ Is safety and emergency equipment appropriate, in good working order and maintained?

☑ Do you believe the employee has responsibility to look after a company vehicle, lease or rental car? **If so, think again.** If you require employees to check safety systems, you must document this, train employees how to do the checks and monitor that they do them. It may be better to have internal systems or outsource to competent contractors – in either case, auditing is imperative.

☑ Are appropriate provisions in place for carrying and securing items, goods and equipment in the vehicle? (There are specific legal duties for the carriage of dangerous goods, training and information.)

☑ Do you ensure that staffs are instructed in the use of new vehicle technologies? (Many drivers lack experience in the latest advances.)

☑ Do you ensure that hire car companies provide a user handbook?

☑ Do you provide drivers with guidance on good posture and how to set their seat correctly?

### Driver competence

Are you satisfied that your drivers are competent and capable of doing their work in a way that is safe for them and other people?

☑ Do you assess the driving capabilities of all new drivers, for instance, using online driving assessments? When did your employees last have a driving lesson: was it for their driving test? Safe driving techniques have advanced considerably and 'defensive driver training' is provided by the Institute of Advanced Motorists. Updating driver skills and awareness can be a life-saver and IAM qualifications can also reduce the insurance premium. Employers should put anyone who routinely drives for work through this sort of training with refreshers.

☑ Do you screen driving licences, DVLA records, experience, training records and knowledge of the Highway Code? Do you outsource DVLA vetting? In order to meet Data Protection Act requirements you must use DVLA-accredited contractors.

☑ Do you evaluate whether additional or refresher training is necessary or stipulate company training standards you expect to be met?

☑ Do you prioritise drivers, for instance those who do high mileage or those who are only occasional business drivers?

☑ Do you ensure drivers know how to carry out vehicle checks (tyre pressures, oil and screen wash levels, adjusting headlamp beam to compensate for load, adjusting seat belts and head restraints)?

☑ Do drivers know what action to take in the event of an incident, near miss or vehicle breakdown?

### Fitness

Are you satisfied that your drivers are fit and healthy to drive safely and will not put themselves or others at risk?

☑ Do you ensure drivers know and meet the health and fitness requirements set out by DVLA and the Highway Code?

☑ Are drivers aware of the dangers of fatigue? Do they know what they should do if they are tired or drowsy?

- ☑ Is company policy supportive of driver autonomy regarding breaks and overnight stays? If not, what is the strategy for fatigue management and how is it checked?
- ☑ Do you monitor driving hours? Do you ensure personal appraisals include the management of work-related road risk?

### Distractions

- ☑ Do you consider how to make contact with your drivers? Good employers ban drivers from using hand-held mobile phones or other mobile communication devices and ban or restrict the use of hands-free equipment. They expect drivers to activate their voicemail and make calls when their engine is switched off.
- ☑ Do you explain to your drivers the purpose of any driver monitoring devices or vehicle trackers and ensure their use is positive, not detrimental to safe driving?

### Journey suitability

- ☑ Is the journey necessary? Could the activity be achieved instead via a telecon, video conference, net meeting or webinar, or by using public transport?

### Planning and scheduling

- ☑ Sleep-related accidents are most likely between 02:00-06:00 and 14:00-16:00. Do you consider this when planning work schedules?
- ☑ Are schedules realistic? Do they allow for rest breaks, planned highway maintenance, weather conditions and shift patterns?
- ☑ Are you satisfied that company policy does not put drivers under pressure to work long hours, make excessively long journeys, or take risks (such as exceeding safe speeds) because of agreed arrival times?

F 06

## 5.0 Managing the risks

In addition to providing the risk assessment checklist, the HSE/DfT publication *Driving at risk* reinforces the need for developing a **safe driver policy** and integrated health and safety management arrangements that include monitoring and checking that the policy is applied and works.

There should be **blame-free** mechanisms for reporting incidents, including near-misses and any impacts, regardless of fault. Understanding any **trends** or incident patterns will help target resources to maximise the impact of preventive measures and to investigate (jointly with union health and safety reps) where appropriate help will take forward the lessons learned.

- ☑ Company rules and procedures covering vehicles, drivers, journeys and management.
- ☑ Arrangements for staff consultation and involvement.
- ☑ Safe driving standards and performance indicators.
- ☑ Responsibility for the policy and its enforcement.
- ☑ Resources for compliance.
- ☑ Information gathering and sharing with staff.
- ☑ Arrangements for driver assessment, information, instruction and training.
- ☑ Mobile phone use.
- ☑ Arrangements for tackling fatigue.
- ☑ Surveillance (for example, vehicle tracking and/or driver monitoring devices).

Prospect has experience of many company policies that adopt these key HSE/DfT principles. Only a few go further and create expectations of **careful scheduling and realistic meeting times**. It appears that corporate ideals often flounder within the management chain and become overshadowed by business demands and performance pressures.

Prospect advises reps and members to be alert to the pressures, be they external and from line management or self-imposed from a sense of professional responsibility. It is you who may be at greater risk of an accident and who may unintentionally kill or be killed. So Prospect urges reps to push their employer to consider such policies as:

- ☑ examining work schedules to ensure that drivers are not pressured by time
- ☑ ensuring that staff do not drive long journeys after a full day's work (for instance, by enabling overnight stays for employees attending a distant meeting)
- ☑ limiting in-car distractions.

### Your role in risk management

> **! Road traffic law has primacy over health and safety law**
>
> This means that when you drive, you are likely to be the principal duty holder. There are at least 25 pieces of legislation, guidance and protocol relating to at-work driving, covering a range of matters (such as speed, insurance, vehicle roadworthiness, mobile phone use and drink driving). **You must comply.**

So don't let work pressures undermine your compliance, your driving licence, your health, your employment or the lives of you, your passengers and/or other road users. Assert your right as an employee and your duties as a driver to travel from A to B safely, without putting you or other road users at risk, and without jeopardising your good record or the reputation of your employer.

## Questions you should ask yourself

### Insurance

☑ Do you have the necessary insurance cover for driving on official business? If you are using an official vehicle, carry only official passengers – other passengers may not be insured. If using a hire car that is delivered to your home, check the insurance cover is tailored to your professional needs.

### Competence

☑ When did you last have a driving lesson? Safe driving techniques have advanced considerably and updating your skills and awareness can be a life-saver. If you routinely drive for work, your employer should provide targeted training and refreshers (about every three years is considered sensible).

### Vehicle

☑ If you use your own car, it is likely you will be responsible for ensuring its road worthiness and that routine checks and any required servicing are maintained. Your employer may request proof and you are advised to co-operate. This includes reasonable requests for proof of maintenance and servicing. Some employers now ban the use of private cars to avoid the liability that arises if an employee drives dangerously.

☑ If you are provided with a company or hire car, you may expect your employer's contract with the provider to guarantee road worthiness and maintenance. While this is a reasonable expectation, as a driver you are also expected to make checks.

☑ For hire car users in particular, it makes sense to make safety critical checks prior to your journey. Certainly you must ensure familiarity with vehicle controls before setting off.



**Safety-critical checks include:**

- tyre condition and pressures
- oil and screen wash levels
- lights
- windscreen wipers
- emergency equipment.

A common complaint from members is that a hire car is provided without a handover or handbook. Insist that these are prerequisites to your journey if the vehicle is unfamiliar and leaves you in any doubt as to its operation.

Remember your rights to safety, your duties as an employee to ensure your own safety (and that of others) and your duty to co-operate with your employer. Do not accept a vehicle if you have doubts about its safety. Speaking up for your safety is an essential right.

### Planning

☑ Route planning and weather forecasting are sensible for journeys that are out of the ordinary. This is about considering the most appropriate route, finding out whether there are planned road works, anticipating the weather, having due regard to the likelihood of fatigue and so on.

**The AA has excellent web advice with practical driver tips: for instance, in snow, pull away in second gear to enhance vehicle control. The Transport Direct website journey planner is similarly helpful.**

### Distractions

Safe driving requires your full attention. Drivers are faced with many distractions but many are in-car and therefore within your control, for example:

☑ having a phone conversation

☑ map reading

☑ using mobile communication devices (BlackBerry, laptop and vehicle navigation systems)

☑ changing CDs

☑ loud music (which may mask other sounds)

☑ eating and drinking

☑ arguing with other road users.

**The use of a hand-held phone while driving is now illegal. So too in some circumstances is the use of a hands-free kit.**

Talking on a mobile phone is not like talking to a passenger who is aware of your driving considerations. The likelihood of distraction is greater and may stop you paying attention or maintaining proper control of your vehicle.

The Attorney General has stated in relation to fatal road traffic incidents that:

**... any mobile phone use at the time of an accident, whether hands-free or not, will result in prosecution for death by dangerous driving.**

In the event of an incident the police will check your phone use. It may be work but it's your call whether you take it. **The policy of Prospect and many other companies is therefore: phone ON = engine OFF.**

RoSPA says drivers using their mobile, whether hands-free or not:

- ☑ are less aware of what is happening on the road around them
- ☑ fail to see road signs
- ☑ fail to maintain good road position and steady speed
- ☑ are more likely to tailgate
- ☑ react more slowly and take longer to break
- ☑ are more likely to enter unsafe gaps in traffic
- ☑ get more frustrated and stressed

**....are four times more likely to crash!**



## Fitness

As a licence and duty holder it is for you to ensure you meet the DVLA health and fitness (including eyesight) requirements. High mileage drivers will also wish to have regard for their back health.

## Fatigue

Surveys suggest that as many as 60% of drivers admit to driving while feeling drowsy. Up to 30% have fallen asleep at the wheel and up to 8% have had a road accident due to fatigue. Not surprisingly, studies link accidents to a lack of sleep, and/or poor quality sleep (for instance, when on stand-by) before driving and night-time driving.

**Many accidents occur as drivers return from work, and company car drivers and shift workers are among those identified at greater risk. Higher rates of fatigue-related accidents are associated with monotonous roads, such as motorways.**

Simulator studies suggest the most consistently reported effects include lane meandering, decreases in speed, increases in speed, increased off-road events and slower reaction times.

## Breaks

Research that looked at Prospect energy sector members revealed how common it is for our members to work through breaks, with a third reporting that they never or rarely took the breaks to which they were entitled. The study found that almost three-quarters of drivers regularly experienced fatigue while driving for work and a fifth experienced it frequently.

**For further information refer to the Prospect *Members' guide to working time and the law*.**

## Your attitude

Research shows that company drivers tend to be more hostile to traffic laws, more likely to drive under time-pressure while tired or undertaking distracting or cognitively demanding tasks, and less likely to consider themselves responsible and safe drivers. Their willingness to perform dangerous violations is reportedly greater.

**Prospect reps in the Ministry of Defence report that MOD is using technology to manage driver attitude. An electronic monitoring device with set parameters of vehicle control and speed (such as cornering, braking and acceleration) is fitted to the vehicle to monitor how it is driven and provide instant feedback to the driver, by a green LED on the dashboard indicating good driving; amber warning and red indicating dangerous driving.**

Following a consultation exercise, the system (called 'DRI VES') was accepted by management and Prospect MOD Group as a **positive tool to help lower the risk of accidents**. This type of initiative is expected to be mirrored elsewhere and Prospect can advise about the consultation if requested.

The key point is that road safety law requires you to be in control of your driving. Your compliance with the law, your technique on the road and whether you alarm other road users, including pedestrians, are all **your responsibility and your choice**.

### Emergencies

All vehicles should be equipped with the essentials: a high-visibility vest or jacket, warning triangle, torch, cloth, ice-scraper and/or deicer.

As a duty holder, you should know what to do in the event of vehicle breakdown. Refresh yourself if necessary by looking at the advice in the *Travel and transport* Directgov web pages or those provided by the AA. Remember, special care is required to deal with a motorway breakdown, because:

- the risk of a fatal or serious accident to an occupant of a parked vehicle is about three times that of driving along the motorway
- 32% of accidents on the hard shoulder are fatal or serious, compared with 13% of all motorway accidents
- on average around 50 people every year are killed or seriously injured in hard shoulder accidents.

Consider storing the leaflet *Surviving the hard shoulder* from the Survive group website in your glove box as a reminder should you need it.

F 06

## 6.0 Experience from the courts

Criminal and civil case law arising from prosecutions, litigation and personal injury claims has strongly influenced work-related road risk management and the expectations of insurance companies for their clients. Members need to be alive to developments.

### Vehicle maintenance

It used to be the case that liability for road traffic accidents involving a work vehicle rarely went beyond the driver. However, increasingly the courts have recognised that a work vehicle falls under the Provision and Use of Work Equipment Regulations. As such, the previous degree of protection from claims enjoyed by car leasing and rental companies has changed. They used to be regarded as mere owners of the vehicle and their maintenance contractors. This is no longer the case. For instance, a garage was blamed for a fatal crash because it failed to carry out a proper service and check the braking system.

Indeed, for daily rental it is unlikely that the courts will now place any responsibility for checking safety-critical systems upon occasional drivers. It may be different for longer hires, but in this case employers are likely to have to train the driver as to what to check, when and how.

### Long hours and fatigue

Pressures to work long hours and the risks of driver fatigue are taken seriously by the courts.

- In one case, the judge remarked that a managing director's words of 'eating's cheating!' and 'you can sleep when you're dead' summed up the company's philosophy. Companies need to be sure that their employees are in a fit condition to drive and have had adequate quality sleep before getting behind the wheel.
- In another case, a company was fined £30,000 after it admitted breaching health and safety law following the fatal crash of an employee who had worked four consecutive 19-hour days and the previous 11 days without a day off.
- A road haulage company manager was jailed in one case for failing to prevent his drivers from working excessive hours; but so too was the driver, for causing death by dangerous driving. So both driver and employer can face criminal prosecution.

### How much work is too much for employees to drive?

A driver was returning home from Yorkshire to Bournemouth on the day of an incident which occurred around 23:00. In Hampshire the driver struck a recovery truck and killed a man working under a parked car. The jury in the trial heard that the driver had been awake for more than 16 hours at the time of the incident. In sentencing her, the judge noted that she must have fallen asleep at the wheel but he did not believe that when she set out she realised she was as tired as she obviously was.

**16 hours of wakefulness** is seen by many employers as an absolute limit in expecting people to work and then drive. It is good practice to consider this limit when agreeing risk assessments.

### Mobile phones

#### Case study 1

An employee spent 6½ minutes on his hand-held mobile phone (while driving his own car for work) during a 15-minute journey in which he ignored 15 road signs. He then made an illegal turn onto the M6 motorway, killing a motorcyclist driving in the opposite direction. He was jailed for five years followed by a five-year driving ban. His employer escaped prosecution because the call was to the driver's wife, and not a business call.

#### Case study 2

An employee using a hand-held mobile phone lost control of his car and collided with another, killing its driver. He received a three-year jail sentence plus a four-year driving ban. His employer was able to show that the policy and procedures were in line with good practice and that specific instructions had been issued to all employees regarding the use of mobile phones while driving. The employer was therefore cleared of any blame.

## 7.0 Research

Research suggests that company car drivers who regularly drive at least once a week have an increased road accident liability of around 40% to 50% above ordinary drivers. A number of theories have been advanced to explain this, including high mileage, the use of new high performance cars, low personal costs in terms of repairs and inconvenience, personality traits (such as aggression and extraversion) and organisational factors (such as time pressure and work-related fatigue).

Studies that have explored risk-taking behaviour suggest that company car users drive faster than other road users and often exceed the speed limit. Those who do so frequently consider arriving on time to be more important than exceeding the speed limit.

Others have identified that time pressure has an important influence on driving behaviour, suggesting that organisational changes that reduce time pressures might be beneficial. However, others have suggested that since the increased accident liability of company car drivers appears to extend to non-work driving, then driving style should also be addressed.

More recent studies highlight the significance of the safety culture of an organisation, as lower accident rates have been found in companies with clear policies, rules, formal training and effective communication and reporting systems compared to companies that do not. Relatively few studies have explored these issues in any detail.

## 8.0 Useful references

www.

**For further information on safe driving and work-related road risk refer to the following topics and associated websites.**

- ☑ **Travel and transport, including the Highway Code.**
- ☑ **HSE road safety.**
- ☑ **Think! Fatigue pages.**
- ☑ **Driving for Better Business.**
- ☑ **ROSPA road safety.**
- ☑ **IAM road safety.**

F
06

# 07
# House building

Contents

## Overview

**The nature of house building can give rise to additional challenges, such as working in and around live residential environments, tight site logistics, fast-track programmes, changing contractor workforce, finishing trades working in close proximity to each other in small spaces, and security and theft.**

**This chapter highlights some of the main issues. However, most topics encountered on site are common issues and are addressed in other sections of GE 700.**

## 7.1 Introduction

House building is a major component of the overall construction industry in Great Britain and, whilst much of the management guidance provided in this publication can be applied to the work carried on in housing developments, there are some subtle differences.

The Home Builders Federation's (HBF) Health and Safety forum has developed a charter and action plan for driving continuous improvements in the home building industry. The overall objectives are to agree principles that the industry can work to, and to work collaboratively to learn from each other's experiences and improve health and safety performance.

**For further information refer to the Home Builders Federation's website.**

The forum also collects accident and incident statistics from its membership that, year on year, has provided the industry with information on which to respond. For example, a combined campaign with the Health and Safety Executive (HSE) to reduce the number of slips and trips in the industry was a direct result of the findings from these statistics.

In addition to analysing and responding to these statistics, house builders are continually striving to ensure that the requirements of relevant and current health and safety legislation and regulations are interpreted and implemented in a manner that removes and reduces the risk of ill health and injury to its workforce and to those who are affected by its work.

In order to achieve this, the likes of the HBF Health and Safety forum work closely with the HSE and other trade bodies to ensure that they have a positive input into guidance produced by these organisations, which takes into account the needs of house builders.

**Good examples of this can be found when working with the following organisations.**

- ☑ **UKTFI (timber frame fire safety).**
- ☑ **Strategic Forum for Plant Safety (manoeuvring of roof trusses).**
- ☑ **The National Federation of Roofing Contractors (controlling silica when disc cutting roof tiles).**
- ☑ **The Building Products Delivery Working Group (Delivering safely – Guidance for the delivery and receipt of building products).**

## 7.2 Important points

In general the requirements placed on house builders to assess risks in line with the Management Regulations in order to manage work that falls under operational regulations (such as Work at Height, PUWER, LOLER, Manual Handling and PPE) are no different to those covered by GE 700.

However, because of the progressive nature of the build programme on housing developments, which sees the introduction of customers onto site whilst construction continues, the CDM Regulations become more relevant to house builders.

Many house builders take on the combined role of numerous duty holders detailed in the CDM Regulations (for example, a house builder with technical, commercial and construction departments can very often act as the client, principal designer and principal contractor).

Whilst establishing duty holder competency through training and experience is a priority, it is the requirements in Part 4 of the regulations that sets house building apart from large-scale one-off projects that can be more easily protected. In particular the proper management of vehicle movement, pedestrian segregation and public protection are of prime consideration.

### 7.2.1 HBF accident statistics

www.

**The HBF has a comprehensive recording system and produces an annual report on health and safety statistics, provided by a number of its volume house building member organisations, which is available on the HBF website.**

The organisations that contribute to these statistics confirm that each year, on average there are 70,000 people employed on their sites and over 300 reportable accidents, of which one third are reportable specified injuries.

The top four causes are shown below.

- ☑ Slips, trips and falls on the same level (33%).
- ☑ Falls from height (23%).
- ☑ Manual handling (16%).
- ☑ Being hit by an object (13%).

### 7.2.2 Slips, trips and falls on the same level

Of all the incidents reported to the HSE, 33% were attributable to slips, trips and falls on the same level. Three main areas, shown below, contributed to over 50% of these.

- ☑ Materials.
- ☑ Scaffold use.
- ☑ Steps and stairways.

Maintaining good housekeeping, clear access routes and tidy working areas are basic controls that help accident prevention and productivity.



## 7.3 Planning

The planning of any development, including compound set up, show-house area, car parking, welfare, and so on, at the outset is an important factor in the management of health and safety. Often, however, the progressive sale of new homes can dictate and alter the speed and direction of build and ongoing changes to plans require careful management.

Any house building site manager therefore needs to employ sound, ongoing monitoring systems to ensure that neither the workforce nor members of the public are put at risk by the sequence of build.

The major items for ongoing review are shown below.

- ☑ **Site security (out of hours).** Ensure boundary fences are maintained to prevent access by unauthorised persons to build areas. Children and teenagers are inquisitive and reasonable attempts must be made to keep them out and to protect them from any hazards that are on site (such as securing down manhole covers and blocking off ladders or access towers).

  By the very nature of house building, the materials, fixtures and fittings are desirable to thieves and the risk of theft is high, particularly as the build enters the final stages. Measures should reflect the increased risk, especially as fencing and storage areas reduce.

- ☑ **Site security (during work hours).** Ensure that site entrances and exits clearly indicate that unauthorised access is not permitted. This may, in some circumstances, require the need for a gate person.

www.

**The HSE has produced some interactive case studies for building sites, giving examples of unsafe practices and how they can be corrected at the planning stage.**

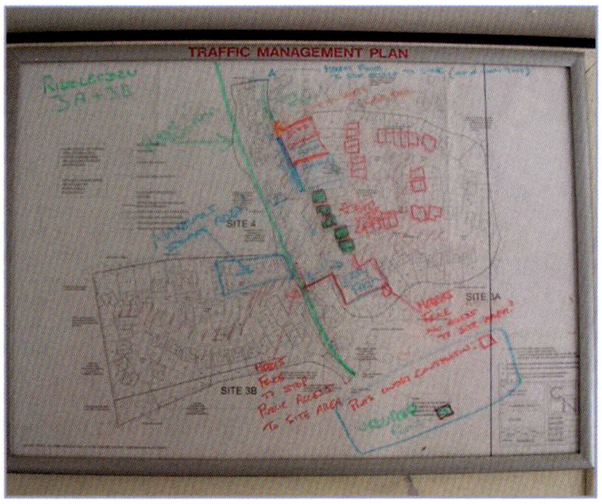


- **Traffic management (pedestrian).** Safe pedestrian routes, both within the work area for site operatives and adjacent footpaths used by members of the public. Consideration should be given to how the public used the area before development started, to ensure they do not ignore signage and continue as before.
- **Traffic management (vehicles).** Clear signage and vehicle routes should be established with speed limits and restraints where necessary. One-way systems should, wherever possible, be established and the reversing of vehicles should remain at a minimum.
- **Traffic management (deliveries).** Material delivery areas should be established taking into account turning points, use of marshals, and so on. Consideration should be given to routes that pass through residential areas, especially housing developments, taking into account public and home owners' vehicles and peak periods of traffic movement (such as commuting and school runs).

**Consortium agreement pro-formas, for use by house builders developing the same site, are effective tools for identifying agreement on collective controls (such as traffic management and site security). These can be found on the HBF website.**

**All the above points will need careful re-evaluation once new homes become occupied and the dynamics of the development change.**

Phased construction work and completion of new homes within developments is generally planned at pre-start meetings but progress can be changed dependent on sales, and therefore site planning will be regularly reviewed as part of any house builder's site review process, as plots are released for sale.



## 7.4 Common house building issues

### 7.4.1 Deliveries

The Building Products Delivery Working Group (BPDWG) has produced a leaflet *Delivering safely – Guidance for the delivery and receipt of building products,* and have acknowledged the support of the HSE in writing this.

It represents good practice, which may go further than the minimum needed to comply with the law.

The leaflet is designed to help delivery drivers and site managers understand what is required to ensure the safe delivery of building products across the building products delivery industry.

***Delivering safely*** **can be downloaded from the BPDWG website.**

### 7.4.2 Roof trusses

Following the publication of the HSE Information sheet WPT14, the major suppliers of trusses to the industry now follow this, to minimise fall risks during the unloading of roof trusses.

**For further information on unloading roof trusses refer to Appendix A.**

This guidance removes the risk of falls and as such the use of fall prevention measures (such as crash decks) and fall protection measures (such as airbags and safety nets) are kept to a minimum.

If a telehandler is being used for lifting and travelling with roof trusses, it should be remembered that this is not the primary purpose of telehandlers. When selecting equipment for this activity the first step should be to ensure that a telehandler is suitable for carrying out the task safely. Where other equipment is more suitable, it should be used.

The lifting of suspended loads with telehandlers and travelling with those loads is generally more hazardous than lifting unit loads on the forks of a telehandler.

www.

**Refer to the Strategic Forum for Plant Safety website for guidance on using a telehandler for manoeuvring roof trusses.**

**For further information on the safe use of vehicles on construction sites refer to the HSE website.**

In addition to this guidance the HBF Health and Safety forum has produced accompanying guidance for the manoeuvring of roof trusses by telehandlers.

**For further information and extracts refer to Appendix B.**

## 7.4.3 Stairwells and open joists

The risk of falls through open joists, working around open stairwells and fall risks during the installation of staircases and banisters must all be assessed and physically controlled on site. The use of birdcage scaffolds, bespoke decking systems, stairwell working platforms, bespoke handrail systems and fall-arrest systems (such as soft-landing systems) are available for use in these instances.

## 7.5 Work at height

Almost every house building project will involve the main contractor or their respective trade contractors in working at height. Statistics clearly illustrate that working at height is a major cause of accidents.

The Work at Height Regulations encompasses all work where 'a fall that is likely to cause injury may occur', including deliveries, roof work and falls into excavations. The scope of the regulations include all types of access equipment and work platforms, regardless of how long an employee is at height, or of the height at which the activity occurs.

Some examples in a house building environment that can be classified as working at height are shown below.

- ☑ Working on any type of scaffold.
- ☑ Being on the back of a lorry or raised loading bays.
- ☑ Working close to an excavation or trench.
- ☑ Working off steps, hop ups or mobile towers.
- ☑ Mezzanine floors with no edge protection.
- ☑ Installing roof trusses or working above open joists.
- ☑ Stairwells with no stairs or staircases with no handrails.
- ☑ Temporary wheelbarrow ramps onto the back of skips.
- ☑ Working off external scaffold, building walls while there is no fall prevention or protection on the internal side of the wall or room, and especially across window openings.

**For further information on working at height refer to:**

- ☑ **Chapter D01 Work at Height Regulations**
- ☑ **Chapter D05 Fall arrest and suspension equipment.**

F 07

## Examples of poor work at height practice

*Poor use of soft-landing system*

*Missing midrails, toe-boards and loose boards*

*Poor stairwell edge protection and working access*

*Incorrect scaffold access, ramp and edge protection*

## Examples of good work at height practice

*Good standard of access scaffold*

*Birdcage system*

*Crash decking system*

*Soft-landing system*

*Stairwell access platform (viewed from ground floor)*

*Stairwell access platform (viewed from first floor)*

## 7.6 Fire

Fire is an ever-present threat throughout the majority of construction and demolition projects. As house building progresses the nature of the fire risk is likely to change as different work starts and is completed. Therefore, not only must the risk of fire be managed continuously, but the management process must allow for the changing nature of the risk.

**For further guidance refer to Chapter C02 Fire prevention and control.**

### 7.6.1 Common sources of fire risk

- Storage and use of flammable materials, including liquefied petroleum gas (LPG).
- Hot work.
- Electrical systems and equipment, including temporary lighting.
- Arson.
- Smoking.
- Operating plant and equipment.
- Poor housekeeping.

**It is vital that the project fire strategy takes into account occupied homes, fire hydrant points and emergency fire and rescue vehicle access.**

### 7.6.2 Specialist advice

The Fire Protection Association (FPA), in conjunction with the Construction Confederation (CC), published the eighth edition of *Fire prevention on construction* sites in July 2012. This joint Code of Practice (CoP) deals with the protection from fire on construction sites and buildings undergoing renovation.

The CoP does not have any legal status; however, it does outline good practice and many insurance companies now require that the authoritative guidelines (such as those detailed in the CoP) are properly implemented on construction projects before they will give full insurance.

The FPA also publishes *Construction site fire prevention checklist – a guide for insurers, surveyors and construction industry professionals*.

### 7.6.3 Timber frames

All timber-frame construction is deemed high risk and additional precautions must be taken.

**Guidance can be found in the HSE publication *Fire safety in construction* (HSG168), which can be downloaded free from its website.**

The **UK Timber Frame Association** (UKTFA)'s ***Site safe*** is the industry leading initiative that allows the construction community to reap all the benefits of timber-frame construction in any urban location while mitigating the risk of arson during construction.

The *Site safe* strategy has many component parts. Together these form a comprehensive set of guidelines that are reliant on the collaborative working of the entire construction supply chain to reduce the risk of fire on timber-frame construction sites.

*Site safe* ensures UKTFA manufacturing member companies that are working on large projects give clear, concise information and assistance to the principal contractor regarding fire safety on construction sites.

It also ensures that all contractors involved in timber-frame sites are fully briefed on identifying fire risks during the construction phase. While the responsibility for addressing the fire risk lies with the principal contractor, *Site safe* provides a framework through which any risk can be consistently communicated so that appropriate action can be taken.

*Site safe* is formed in three parts.

| | |
|---|---|
| **Design phase** | RIBA plan of works A – E |
| **Project construction/procurement phase** | RIBA plan of works F – H |
| **On-site phase** | RIBA plan of works J – K |

**UKTFA has also produced guidance called *16 steps to fire safety on timber-frame construction sites.* This practical guidance should be read in conjunction with the above FPA publications.**

The UKTFA guidance also contains a risk assessment flowchart, which helps identify site security measures required, depending upon the fire-resisting sub-division of the building.

By following the flowchart (which asks such questions about the building as 'Is it more or less than three storeys?' and 'What is the building footprint shape and dimensions?') the outcome is rated A to C and the minimum security arrangements are shown in the table below.

| Security level | Security features |
|---|---|
| Security package A | Non-climbable perimeter fencing and locked site and building access outside of site hours |
| Security package B | Security package A, plus out-of-hours security guards and movement-sensitive security lighting |
| Security package C | Security package B, plus CCTV, permanent security lighting and all ground-floor openings secured |

## 7.7 Construction dust

Many house building works will give rise to dust, which should be considered a high health risk. Each year thousands of construction workers contract or die from respiratory diseases due to breathing in dust and fumes.

The amount breathed in each day as they work from site to site can seem small or insignificant. In some cases the effects of exposure may be immediate but generally it can take years before the symptoms of ill health become apparent. Because of this, respiratory risks are often overlooked or underplayed.

Typical work that creates harmful levels of dust includes the following.

- ☑ Sweeping a dusty floor.
- ☑ Mechanically cutting, chasing or drilling concrete, bricks and blocks.
- ☑ Mixing sand and cement to make mortar.
- ☑ Sanding down MDF or timber.
- ☑ Rubbing down tape and jointing or plaster.



**All dusts are hazardous to health. The creation of dust, regardless of amount, must be controlled – all risk assessments and method statements should state how exposure to dust or fumes will be minimised. It is no longer acceptable to expect workers to work unprotected in dusty conditions.**

**For further information, from an environmental perspective, refer to Section E: *Environment* or for the related ill health issues refer to Chapter B10 Dust and fumes.**

Cutting roof tiles in valleys has historically created a lot of silica dust, which is hazardous to health. The National Federation of Roofing Contractors (NFRC) has issued recent guidance on this that clearly identifies the controls, including separate cutting areas and suitable dust suppression, which should be in place during this work activity.

**The NFRC guidance sheet *Controlling silica when disc cutting roof tiles* can be downloaded free from its website.**

**The construction dust partnership provides information to industry to promote good practice and reduce dust related diseases.**

Cutting of other housing development building materials that produce dust (such as using petrol cut-off saws on kerbs and paving slabs) must be done using methods to eliminate or minimise dust (such as using a block splitter, using water suppression or dust extract systems).

It is recognised good practice to use respiratory protective equipment (RPE) with an FFP3 or P3 rating to protect against all construction dust (such as silica) that is created when mechanically cutting concrete, bricks, slabs, and so on – even when wet cutting (which only removes about 75% of airborne particles). FFP3/P3 offers maximum protection compared to FFP1/P1 or FFP2/P2.

**When using RPE with tight-fitting facepieces ensure that each wearer has a face-fit test.**

**For further guidance on how to manage dust and fumes refer to Chapter B10 Dust and fumes.**

## 7.8 Environmental considerations

When planning and monitoring the works, environmental impacts must be assessed.

**These are covered in Section E: *Environment*, together with practical guidance on how to identify and manage important risks.**

Consideration should also be given to how work could impact on the local community, especially nuisance.

### 7.8.1 Mud

Mud and dust can be difficult to manage, and be made worse by unexpectedly prolonged wet weather or dry spells.

*Early installation of roads, footpaths and driveways on site reduces construction mud and dust on and off site*

Mud can be carried far along a road, with large lumps being a hazard to cyclists and motorbikes and wet mud making the road slippery, especially in wet, cold and dark weather. Roads must be kept clear, using measures from a spade and broom, to hiring a road sweeper.

Installing roads, footpaths and driveways early in a project can help to reduce mud and protect people from tripping over on uneven ground. It also provides a better standard of housekeeping and safer storage.

**Road brush attachments are available, which can be fitted quickly to the forks of a telehandler. Having one on site means roads can be regularly cleaned as and when required.**

### 7.8.2 Dust

Mud can quickly turn to dust, and in dry conditions dust can swirl and carry in the wind, quickly covering neighbouring properties and vehicles. Efforts must be made to dampen down site and road surfaces.

### 7.8.3 Local community

Proactively keeping local communities and residents informed of what is happening is far more productive than dealing with complaints, which can quickly escalate. Taking the time and effort early on (such as attending parish meetings, knocking on doors and introducing the site manager, or regular letter drops) can pay off in the long-term.

*Community engagement*

Letters can contain information on items such as large deliveries or the increased number of vehicle movements, any weekend work and why the changes have become necessary, together with contact information.

Engaging with the community should also be encouraged (such as carrying out safety talks at local schools or supporting a local community project).

# Appendix A – Unloading roof trusses

**The following case study is based upon the HSE Information sheet *Unloading roof trusses* (WPT14), which gives examples of good practice to reduce injuries due to falls from vehicles through sensible management of health and safety risks in the workplace.**

## The challenge

During a manufacturer's delivery of roof trusses, it was identified that customers had problems when unloading trussed rafters from the lorry by crane.

Slingers were required to climb the trusses on the lorry to cut the securing ropes. They were then required to attach the sling or chains to the truss and connect them to the crane before sliding back down from the truss.

## Finding a solution

Introduction of a colour coded banding system.

- ☑ **Blue bands** are now used to secure the trusses into bundles.
- ☑ **White bands** secure the trussed rafters to the vehicle frame.

This development eliminated the risk of the wrong band being cut during the unloading process. The drivers, who have been issued with telescopic cutting poles, now have no need to climb onto the lorry.

The next development was the introduction of **sacrificial slings** attached at the factory. As these are easy to get to from the ground by the slingers there is again no need to climb onto the vehicle.

## Results

- ☑ The introduction of these measures has eliminated the risk of falls from vehicles.
- ☑ In addition, as there is now no requirement for the use of fall-arrest systems, there have been savings in time and money.
- ☑ Customers are now able to unload vehicles more quickly and safely.

**Further information can be found on the workplace transport and falls sections of the HSE website.**

# Appendix B – Manoeuvring roof trusses

**The information below is based on manoeuvring of roof trusses guidance developed by members of the Home Builders Health and Safety forum, which is available to download from the HBF website.**

## Transporting or manoeuvring trusses

The following options can be applied to the transport, manoeuvring and placement of trusses on site.

All roof trusses should be delivered on vehicles in such a manner that operatives do not need to access the rear of vehicles to remove straps or attach lifting strops.

Where practicable, trusses should be lifted directly from the delivery vehicle onto the roof (such as just-in-time delivery); this will require planning of both the site and delivery of trusses and should be the primary method of delivery and lifting.

Where just-in-time deliveries cannot be achieved (for example, if the plot is not ready) trusses should be lifted from the delivery vehicle via the telehandler onto truss racks designed on loading bays or gable end scaffolds. The delivery vehicle should be positioned as close as possible to the plot under construction and the distance to be travelled by the telehandler limited. The storage of trusses must not impede the safe operation of the telehandler or access to the loading bays.

If the above is not practicable and/or access to the construction area is restricted for the delivery vehicle, the trusses can be lifted from the vehicle onto an appropriately designed, freestanding storage rack. The rack should be positioned close to the plots under construction to limit the distance the trusses need to be moved when required. The truss rack should be continually re-sited as close to the work area, where possible, and be easy to get to by delivery vehicles.

## Lifting of trusses onto the wall plate

In the majority of circumstances, lifting of roof trusses should be undertaken by a mobile crane where a full pack can be lifted directly onto the wall plate. A lifting plan completed by an appropriately trained appointed person would be required for the lift.

If an alternative method is utilised to lift roof trusses onto a roof, then this will need to be justified by the completion of a lifting plan for each plot, by an appropriately trained appointed person, which will take the following into consideration.

- ☑ Capabilities of the lifting appliance.
- ☑ Any restrictions to the lifting operation (such as scaffolding or other obstructions).
- ☑ Height of the structure.
- ☑ Handling the trusses by workers on the scaffold working platform.
- ☑ Method of lifting the trusses safely, including consideration of the pitch, size and weight of the truss.

## Transporting of trusses via a telehandler

The following conditions apply if trusses are to be suspended via the forks of a telehandler and transported on a development.

- ☑ The route from the truss rack or delivery vehicle to the plot should not be through occupied areas of the development where practicable. If this is necessary a traffic marshal(s) will be required to ensure occupants or others are not put at risk from the movement of the trusses.
- ☑ The route should be reviewed prior to transporting the trusses and an assessment made if any obstacles (such as lamp posts or scaffold) will affect the ability of the operator to manoeuvre the telehandler and load safely.
- ☑ The maximum load of trusses that can be transported via a telehandler from a truss rack or delivery vehicle to a plot is 600 kg. The weight of all trusses installed on site should be known by site management and detailed in the lifting plan. This is the maximum load, but this may need to be reduced depending on the span/pitch of the trusses, potential obstructions, gradients/cross slopes and capabilities of the machine.
- ☑ The tyre pressures should be within +/- 5% of the maximum stated by the manufacturers and be checked prior to moving the load.
- ☑ The telehandler should be driven at no more than 7 mph with no sharp turns or manoeuvres.
- ☑ The operator should have full vision from the driving position and the trusses suspended from the forks so that the lowest point of the truss (top chord overhang) is within 500 mm (+/- 150 mm) of the ground. A banksman should be available, where there are obstacles to full visibility, to provide appropriate signals to the operator and ensure no other persons are affected by the movement of the trusses.

Trusses should not be moved when wind speeds at ground level are forecast to be or exceed 7 m/s or 16 mph. This should be assessed by the use of an anemometer and/or weather reports for the area.

### Basic telehandler operator training does not include lifting or travelling with suspended loads

If these tasks are to be carried out the employer must ensure that the operator is suitably trained and assessed as competent. The majority of basic training courses only deal with fork-mounted unit loads. Only training providers who can demonstrate having appropriate expertise of suspended loads and lifting operations with telehanders or mobile cranes should be selected. Any training should also include an appropriate element of slinging and signalling.

# Index